RSPB Guide to
Birdwatching

RSPB Guide to
Birdwatching

Peter Conder

Hamlyn

London · New York · Sydney · Toronto

Line drawings by Norman Arlott

Photographic Acknowledgements

Front jacket – Hamlyn Group – Tony Taylor
Back jacket – Bruce Coleman Ltd. – D. & K. Urry

Black and white photographs
Ardea 85; Ardea – J. A. Bailey 143; Ardea – Ian Beames 43;
Ardea – J. B. & S. Bottomley 83; Ardea – C. R. Knights 109;
Ardea – J. P. Laub 117; Bruce Coleman Ltd. – E. Duscher 79;
Peter Conder 54; Hamlyn Group – John Howard 15, 29, 31;
Eric Hosking 49, 61, 84, 106;
Natural History Photographic Agency – D. N. Dalton 125;
Royal Society for the Protection of Birds – Richard T. Mills 128;
Wash Wader Ringing Group – R. C. Hanaford 102.

Colour photographs
Aerofilms Ltd. – 152 top; Ardea – 47 bottom, 97 bottom, 99 bottom;
Ardea – J. A. Bailey 150–151 bottom; Ardea – I. Beames 47 top;
Ardea – J. B. & S. Bottomley 28 top;
Ardea – M. D. England 99 bottom;
Frank V. Blackburn 46, 48 bottom, 98 bottom, 100;
Bruce Coleman Ltd. – S. Dalton 149;
Bruce Coleman Ltd. – Dennis Green 45 bottom;
Bruce Coleman Ltd. – D. & K. Urry 45 top, 48 top;
Bruce Coleman Ltd. – J. van Wormer 150–151 top;
Eric Hosking 27 top and bottom, 28 bottom, 98 top,
99 top, 152 bottom; Jacana 25; Natural History Photographic Agency –
J. Jeffrey 97 top; Wildlife Studies Ltd. – 26 top.

The map of the Nightingale distribution on page 29 and photograph of *Breeding Birds of Britain and Ireland* on page 31 are reproduced by permission of T. & A. D. Poyser.
The field lists on page 15 are reproduced by permission of the British Trust for Ornithology.

Published by
The Hamlyn Publishing Group Limited
London · New York · Sydney · Toronto
Astronaut House, Feltham, Middlesex, England
Copyright © The Hamlyn Publishing Group Limited 1978

ISBN 0 600 31423 5

Phototypeset by
Photocomp Ltd, Birmingham, England
Printed by
Hazell Watson and Viney Ltd,
Aylesbury, Buckinghamshire

Foreword

This *RSPB Guide to Birdwatching* has been prepared as a companion volume to the successful *RSPB Guide to British Birds* published in 1975. The first stage in birdwatching obviously must be to identify the birds one is looking at and this is the function of the first of our guides. But birdwatching, like all good hobbies, has a great deal more to offer. As it is one of the fastest-growing outdoor activities it would appear that a lot of beginners do indeed want to make the most of all that birds can offer and so we were encouraged to produce this second guide.

Like its predecessor, the new guide has been carefully designed to help and interest the beginner – both young and adult. It provides, in a clear and simple manner, all the necessary information required to enable the enthusiast to expand his or her knowledge. The first part covers such things as equipment, field behaviour and ways of counting bird numbers. The second part of the book deals with evolution, anatomy, migration, ringing, nesting behaviour and ecology generally. Finally bird gardening and conservation are discussed.

We could hardly have chosen a better author than Peter Conder, my predecessor as the RSPB's Director. He has worked for most of his life with birds and their protection and he combines the skill of the professional with the enthusiasm of the amateur.

Ian Prestt

Director, Royal Society for the
Protection of Birds

Preface

Whilst it is almost certainly true that you can come closer to birds in the field when you are alone, a more complete knowledge and understanding of birds and birdwatching is something that can only be increased through the experiences and companionship of other birdwatchers. I have been lucky in my teachers in my schooldays, when I was a POW and in the days that followed – from them all I have learnt much. In writing this book I am particularly grateful to Dr Colin Bibby and Nicholas Hammond of the RSPB staff who read through the original manuscript, commented on the accuracy and contents of the book and made many helpful suggestions. Miss Dorothy Rook, until recently Librarian at the RSPB was consistently skilful in finding references for me. David Newham and Richard F. Porter commented on the contents of the original synopsis. To all these friends I owe an immense debt of gratitude: where the text is still in default the responsibility is mine. Finally, my heartfelt thanks to my wife Patricia who sorted out my writing and typed the manuscript, saving me that most tedious chore.

P. C.

Acknowledgements

During the course of writing this book I made reference not only to those books which are to be found in the Appendices but to books or papers written by the following authors or organizations:—
E. A. Armstrong; Robert Bakker; R. J. H. Beverton; N. J. B. Branson & C. D. T. Minton; British Ornithologists' Union; British Trust for Ornithology; B. F. Brockway; D. M. Broom; L. Brown; P. E. Brown; Dr J. Chervas; M. Chinery; Gwen Davies; Peter Davies; W. J. A. Dick; C. E. Johnson; D. I. Sales & A. Zahavi; H. Dobinson; J. Dorst; D. M. Turner-Ettlinger; Camille Ferry; R. S. R. Fitter; J. J. M. Flegg & G. Link; P. H. T. Hartley; J. J. Hickey; R. A. Hinde; Eric Hosking & John Gooders; D. C. Hume; J. S. Huxley; P. Hope Jones; C. J. Mead & R. F. Durman; A. S. King & Jo McCelland; D. Lack; A. Landsborough Thomson; von Bernd Leisler; A. Leopold; C. Lloyd; E. Mayr; I. Newton; Nature Conservancy Council; E. Odum; Myrfyn Owen; P. S. Palmer; Dr C. Perrins; R. T. Peterson; O. S. Pettingill; John Phillipson; Royal Society for the Protection of Birds; A. A. Saunders; David Saunders; E. Selous; David Snow; Society for the Promotion of Nature Conservation; W. H. Thorpe; N. Tinbergen; John Warham; P. & E. Willson; W. B. Yapp.

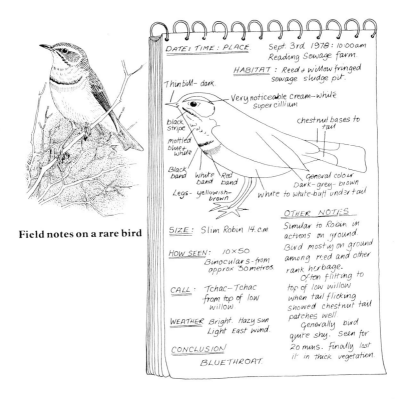

Field notes on a rare bird

DATE: TIME: PLACE Sept. 3rd 1978 : 10:00am
Reading Sewage farm.

HABITAT : Reed + willow fringed sewage sludge pit.

Thin bill - dark.

Very noticeable cream-white super cillium

black stripe

mottled blue + white

Black band White band Red band

Legs - yellowish-brown

chestnut bases to tail

General colour Dark-grey-brown
white to white-buff under tail

SIZE : Slim Robin 14. cm

HOW SEEN : 10 × 50 Binoculars - from approx 30 metres.

CALL : Tchac - Tchac from top of low willow

WEATHER Bright. Hazy Sun Light East wind.

CONCLUSION

BLUETHROAT.

OTHER NOTES
Similar to Robin in actions on ground. Bird mostly on ground among reed and other rank herbage.
Often flitting to top of low willow when tail flicking showed chestnut tail patches well
Generally bird quite shy. Seen for 20 mins. Finally lost it in thick vegetation.

Whenever you see a bird you cannot identify you should write a full description of its plumage, shape, behaviour, calls and habitat before you refer to a field guide.

since paper has become so expensive page margins have become narrower. However, if you go to bookbinding classes you could get your county bird list interleaved, so that you can add your own new and additional records.
Field notebooks Together with a pair of binoculars and a field guide the most important aid that a birdwatcher will need is a field notebook. This, as the name implies, is for use in the field, and is used to record the essential facts of any observation, as well as comments or impressions while they are still fresh in the mind.

The field notebook may take a number of different forms, although it obviously must be small enough to fit easily into your pocket. It may be a cheap notebook that you can throw away when it is filled and the information has been transferred to a more permanent system of recording.

On the other hand a pocket-sized loose-leaf notebook can be very useful as the sheets can be transferred directly into one of the structural index systems. I personally use the Lefax system which is very useful for this purpose since it has a wide variety of printed sheets.

It is in the field notebook that you write the details of your sightings. You should never be afraid of recording too much at this stage, as you can analyze and edit the entry when you are writing up your final records. Remember that every observation in the field is unrepeatable. Always record the date, time and place together with the weather conditions. An Ordnance Survey grid map-reference is a useful method of recording the place of your observation. It is also worth noting the number of the ten kilometre square in which you are working since it is often useful for recording the distribution of birds. A new way of recording your observations is by using a portable tape-recorder, this has the advantage of leaving your hands and eyes free to manipulate your binoculars and watch the bird. However, some practice is needed as initially one tends to overuse it.

Final records Whether you write up your records or simply transfer them to another notebook or filing system depends on how you prefer to organize your original observations and, of course, whether the original field notes are legible. Some people never write up the results of their observations, and, indeed, there is little that would need to be done to a simple list of birds. Some birdwatchers, however, like to go further and keep a diary of ornithological events. In one way the 'bird diary' is the simplest method of keeping more permanent records, but it is not always the easiest system from which to retrieve information. In addition to the Lefax field notebook I, personally, use a stiff-backed notebook and write out an index at the end of each volume.

With a loose-leaf system, as with the loose-leaf field notebook, the sheets can be re-arranged according to your needs; for example, all the records on a particular species or a specific locality can be kept together. There is a wide variety of systems involving loose-leaf sheets. Also there are systems which are used widely in the business and scientific world, which can be successfully adapted for use in birdwatching. 'Key-sort' cards which have small holes punched around their edges can be very useful. Each hole can be indexed to a separate subject. If the completed card contains a reference to that subject then the hole is clipped out to the edge. When you want to find all the cards with a reference to 'habitat', for example, you just put a knitting needle in the appropriate hole and lift the cards and all those with open holes will then fall out.

What you record depends on what interests you. If you are a beginner identification problems will almost certainly require you to write down bird descriptions and the excitement of discovering new birds will be reflected in your diary. Later sections and chapters in this book should give you other ideas. But one thing is clear: writing down what one has seen is a wonderful way of developing observational ability and an enquiring mind.

small milled knob. Some prismatic telescopes also have 'zoom' eye-pieces which means that, once you have found the target bird, you can twist that part of the eye-piece and increase the magnification.

The magnification provided by a telescope usually ranges from about $20 \times$ to $60 \times$. However, as the magnification increases the amount of light being transmitted through the lens is reduced, unless the diameter of the object glass is also increased enormously. I have a zoom-lens telescope but I find that I tend to use the lowest magnification – $25 \times$ – in this country. Even in parts of the world where the sun is brighter I rarely use a magnification above $40 \times$. The resolution of detail with the prismatic telescope seems much finer than with the tube type.

Greater magnification, as in binoculars, increases the problems caused by hand-shake and a firm but light tripod with a pan and tilt head is absolutely essential to hold the telescope steady. Incidentally, it should ideally be a black one so that light is not reflected back to the bird you are trying to watch.

The difference between the British and American birdwatcher becomes very apparent when one comes to the use of telescopes. The American 'birders' seem to carry telescopes everywhere, and use them regularly, whereas the British are far less regular in their use of 'scopes. Tripods and telescopes are perhaps less liked because they are more clutter. I recently had a simple sling for my telescope made by a local saddler, it consists of a webbed belt about 2 or 3 centimetres wide and about 150 centimetres long. Two straps of about 15 centimetres in length are fixed to the webbing about 60 centimetres apart – this distance depends on the length of the tripod when in a closed position. The top strap remains strapped round the tripod beneath the pan and tilt head and the second strap clasps the bottom of the legs when the whole tripod is collapsed. The whole lot is easily carried over your shoulders. You have only to undo the bottom strap, deploy the legs and your telescope is ready for action.

Prismatic telescopes are more expensive than the tube telescopes but I think that their better resolution of detail makes them well worth the extra cost. I have used prismatic telescopes since 1954. Although I have peered through tube telescopes since then from time to time I have never been urged to change over to them. Most ornithological magazines carry advertisements by optical dealers, but, perhaps it is best to find a satisfied customer who can recommend a dealer or go to one who gives you the opportunity to try his range of binoculars and telescopes in the field.

Clothing The first point to remember is that although you wish the bird no harm you are in fact a 'hunter' – a hunter of facts about live birds. You do not wish to kill but to observe as closely as possible without frightening the bird. Bright colours for birdwatching, such as the orange or yellow cagoules, therefore, are out. You need to be clothed in greens, browns and greys or the natural colour of that part of the countryside in which you are working. Khaki has not too pleasant memories for the older generation but is an ideal colour; dark greens, olive and browns are also good as a general rule but can stick out conspicuously on a beach or sand dune. Camouflage jackets, suits and hats, which are regularly advertised in the sporting magazines, are extremely useful. The correct sort of outer garments are more often obtainable at a gunsmith's than at a normal clothing store. A hat is essential, particularly if you are fair-haired, but it is also important to break up the outline of your head, to hide your eyes and shade and darken your face. Pigeon-shooters sometimes use a camouflaged face-mask in order to hide the brightly coloured splodge of their face and, if they do it, why should not a keen birdwatcher?

Peter Hartley, who studied camouflage in the last war, wrote an article for the RSPB in 1954 called 'Camouflage for Birdwatchers'. He says that camouflage really means avoiding recognition. Nightjars and Woodcocks, for instance, can crouch in full view and yet not be recognized. Whilst soberly coloured clothing is important, Peter Hartley also points out that there should be a strong tone contrast between garments – a darker coat with lighter-coloured trousers or vice versa. Other points are that a patterned material is less conspicuous than a plain one; a symmetrical object tends to be more conspicuous than an asymmetrical one; also it is particularly important to disguise the shape of your head and shoulders. Any easy way to see what I mean is to observe others when they are birdwatching. Which outfits merge best against a wood or a field, and which part of the body sticks out like a sore thumb? Then decide what could be done to make the other person blend in with the countryside. Nine times out of ten I would guess that it is the pale face of the observer which is most obvious on an otherwise camouflaged person. The best camouflage is made more effective by absolute stillness and slow and gentle movements.

On many of its reserves the RSPB has built hides. However, the reason for wearing naturally coloured clothes and disguising one's features is to obviate the need for a hide when you are birdwatching. Hides are essential for close-up photography or making a detailed study of the nesting behaviour of some species. They are also useful if you are studying an open area such as a pond, but the average birdwatcher will not normally wish to carry a hide around with him. On the other hand, camouflage nets are fairly easy to carry in a haversack. A number of ex-Government nets are still advertized in shooting magazines but they are also easily made using a length of netting (approximately 3×15 metres with a 5-centimetre mesh). At regular intervals strips of grey, brown and green material can be tied to the net. There should be sufficient strips to disguise the observer's outline from the bird while allowing a clear view through the net. Again stillness adds to the effectiveness of the natural coloration. The net can be simply draped over the head and shoulders or tied between trees or bushes.

A second point about clothing is comfort. In winter the pleasure of watching birds can be ruined by getting wet and very chilled. With the waterproof garments available these days it is possible to remain dry even in the heaviest rain, and many coats of suitable colours lined with quilt for extra warmth are advertised in bird and country magazines. Thermal underclothes can also be highly effective during the cold winter months. Some people like cagoules, but for myself I find that they are too noisy, particularly in cold weather, the rustling does not always frighten birds but it does make it much more difficult to hear them. A birdwatcher would never choose for birdwatching some of the fluorescent colours in which cagoules are made for climbers. However, if you are climbing or indulging in some occupation involving risk, you must obey the safety rules for that occupation.

Feet must be kept warm and dry. Whilst it is easy to keep feet dry by using rubber boots it can sometimes be a problem to keep them warm especially if a lot of standing about is entailed. It is now possible to buy socks made of polyester-filled quilted nylon which are especially designed for use in rubber boots and which are extremely effective.

Photography Photography is an enormous subject about which many books have already been written. Two of the most recent are *Wildlife Photography* written by Eric Hosking and John Gooders, and *An Introduction to Bird and Wildlife Photography* by John Marchington and Anthony Clay. I am really writing for the birdwatcher who wants to take photographs but also wants to remain a birdwatcher. Rightly or wrongly I do not think that you can have your heart in both; few people really achieve a high standard both as a bird photographer and as a naturalist. The photographer tends to use his camera and film as a way of re-creating something about birds whereas the ornithologist will be recording and writing up his observations and this creative activity will, perhaps, result in a scientific paper.

I try to make my pictures as technically perfect and aesthetically pleasing as possible but I am not prepared to spend the amount of time that a professional or keen amateur photographer would devote. My results are essentially records of habitats and so on, which complement my notes and are even usable as slides for lectures. When it comes to studying the feeding habits of birds I find I have very little time for photography. However, when I was studying the nesting behaviour of the Wheatear in Pembroke-shire, I occasionally used a camera from a hide to record particular points. Cameras are not really an essential piece of equipment: some birdwatchers have never taken a photograph in their lives. Many birdwatchers use the 35 millimetre single-lens reflex camera. Usually when taking photographs of habitats a 50 millimetre lens is needed but a wide-angled 35 millimetre lens will also give extremely good results. For photographing birds at a distance a long-focus or telephoto lens is essential; lenses with a focal point of 300 or 400 millimetres are most commonly used.

With these lenses a fast shutter speed is necessary, at the very least 1/250 of a second, together with a fast film. However, as you increase the speed you also increase the 'grain' of the processed film emulsion thus losing some of the definition. A useful piece of equipment is a shoulder butt on which to mount the camera, this helps to keep the camera from shaking while still allowing you a great deal of flexibility. If you are in a position to use your camera with a tripod then a slower shutter setting is possible. Having acquired the basic camera you can build up the remainder of your equipment as and when the money becomes available and the need arises.

If you intend to photograph birds at their nest or in more open positions a hide is almost essential. It is possible to buy one but a simple construction is easily within the reach of the average handyman. The photographer must be extremely careful in his approach to the nest and the way he uses his hide. It is important to remember that the welfare of the bird must be your first concern. *The Nature Photographer's Code of Practice* published by the RSPB and the Zoological Photographic Society can be obtained from the RSPB on receipt of a large stamped addressed envelope. Remember, too, that the Protection of Birds Act 1954–67 prohibits the disturbance of birds on the First Schedule of those Acts. The RSPB booklet *Wild Birds and the Law* gives you the information as to which birds are covered by this law and where you should write for a licence.

Tape-recording For me, the tape-recorder is a way of recording an event and I use it both for dictating notes in the field and recording bird sound. With a portable cassette recorder and the correct type of microphone it is possible to make adequate recordings in the field for very little expense. Although convenient for handling in the field these smaller tape-recorders

When using a hide near a nest great care must be taken to move it closer in slow stages so that the birds become accustomed to it.

Hide construction

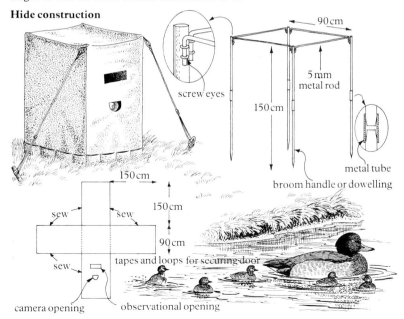

90 cm

5 mm metal rod

150 cm

screw eyes

metal tube

broom handle or dowelling

150 cm

150 cm

90 cm

sew sew

sew

camera opening

observational opening

tapes and loops for securing door

do not produce a very high quality recording. Results can be improved, however, by using a parabolic reflector which collects and concentrates more sound than the microphone alone. It also adds some direction to the microphone and helps to cut out unwanted background noise. For those who wish to go further with this pursuit Richard Margoschis' *Recording Natural History Sounds* (1977) covers most aspects of recording.

Field guides You can watch birds without the help of binoculars and telescopes. Garden birds especially will probably come close enough to enable you to identify them without these aids but unless you have an identification book you cannot satisfy that inquisitive desire that all good naturalists should have, to give a bird its correct name.

As its name suggests a field guide is an identification book that is small enough to carry and refer to in the field. This practice must be followed with care, however, and it is often best to write down a complete description of a bird that is unknown to you, and which could be rare, before you look it up. Otherwise your description may be biased by what you have read. Most of the field guides concentrate on giving only the essential information needed to identify birds in the field and only give the minimum of information about the birds' habitat, song and behaviour. There are plenty of books to choose from but your choice will probably be from the following four.

The RSPB Guide to British Birds, written by David Saunders with paintings by Noel Cusa and published by Hamlyn, is specifically designed for beginners and contains descriptions of only 218 common species of the 500 or so that live in or visit Britain. The advantage of having only a limited number of species to choose from is that the beginner is less likely to be confused by a wide variety of less common birds. However, it is inevitable that once the first stages of identification have been passed and more exotic places are visited that one of three field guides used by birdwatchers all over Europe, will be required. Each of the three has its advantages and disadvantages. None of them is entirely perfect, and with regard to the standard of illustrations, each has its good points and bad points. They are described in alphabetical order of the senior author's name.

The Hamlyn Guide to the Birds of Britain and Europe, written by Bertel Bruun and illustrated by Arthur Singer and published by Hamlyn, describes and pictures in colour 530 birds which you are likely to find in Europe as bordered by the Atlantic, the Mediterranean, the Caspian Sea, the Ural River and Mountains and the Arctic Ocean. The advantage of this book is that the illustrations are opposite the text so that you do not have to switch about over two or even more pages to find out all the relevant information and illustration about the bird. This book has also been extensively revised (1978).

The second book is *The Birds of Britain and Europe, North Africa and the Middle East* which is written by Richard Fitter and John Parslow, illustrated by Herman Heinzel and published by Collins. Like the Hamlyn guide the pictures and text face each other which makes for considerable ease of use. This guide includes all the birds which breed in or visit regularly any part of Europe, north Africa south to a line drawn east from south Morocco and the Middle East to the Persian Gulf and then more or less due north to the Arctic Ocean. It covers a bigger area than any of the other guides and can be of considerable value in countries on the edge of and just outside its defined area. Therefore it is very useful for the traveller, but the large number of species depicted can confuse the beginner in Central Europe.

The third book is the *Field Guide to the Birds of Britain and Europe*, illustrated by Roger Tory Peterson, with text by Guy Mountfort and Philip Hollom, published by Collins. Its major disadvantage is that the text is on a different page from the pictures so that you have to look up at least two pages in the book and sometimes as many as four to get all the information required. This is the older of the modern field guides. Its great advantage is that it has been revised three times and consequently contains very few errors. Furthermore, it is the one guide from which you should be able to identify the bird from the text as well as the illustration. There are other field guides but I think that the ones I have mentioned are amongst the best for the accuracy of illustrations and text. However, there are many other books which specialize in the identification of specific groups of birds and I have listed some in appendix II.

General books After the field guides the book to which I most often refer is *The Popular Handbook of British Birds* by P. A. D. Hollom, published by H. F. & G. Witherby Ltd. It has been through four editions and has been thoroughly revised. In addition to illustrating the bird the book also includes descriptions of the type of habitat, general habits, what is known about the bird's food, its nest, and its status and distribution.

Treating the same subjects but in a rather novel and interesting way is Peter Hayman and Philip Burton's *The Bird Life of Britain* published by Mitchell Beazley. This book combines masses of illustrations with a very informative text; it concentrates mainly on identification but, using the cartoon technique, illustrates nesting habits very well.

The Handbook of the Birds of Britain, Europe and North Africa whose chief author is Stanley Cramp and which was published by the Oxford University Press in 1978, is the most comprehensive book to be published on the birds of this region and contains a considerable amount of detail on the various aspects of each bird's behaviour and biology. It is an excellent book. Each of the seven volumes (only one of which has been published at the time of writing) is expensive in one sense but when balanced against the wealth of information on each page including comprehensive illustration, it is well worthwhile acquiring. Although it covers a wider geographical area it is the successor of the *Handbook of British Birds* whose chief author was H. F. Witherby. This work is now out of print but still contains much valuable material.

The next group of books deals with the general biology and behaviour of birds throughout their life. There are many which survey this field and I

The red-billed Chough searching for ants with its down-curved bill amongst clifftop Thrift on the western cliffs of the British Isles, is one of the ornithological thrills – a unique bird on a rugged coastline.

Left The Bullfinch is a beautiful bird which can cause problems on fruit farms in the south-east of Britain in spring but which eats a wide range of seeds, from chickweed to Ash, at other times of the year.

Left One of the field guides that has made field identification comparatively easy to masses of birdwatchers throughout Europe. The *Hamlyn Guide* has the advantage of text facing the plates.

Right above and right Camouflage is in effect a portable hide. The camouflaged human observer is making himself less recognizable to birds, particularly if he keeps still. Brightly coloured clothes are valuable where a recreation is hazardous – but not when stalking larger birds such as waterfowl.

Above No other bird hovers in quite the same way as the Kestrel. Notice that its head seems fixed to one spot whilst the body will move about in relation to wind strength and direction.

Below The Curlew's long down-curved bill separates it from all but the rather rarer Whimbrel, but its call identifies it at once. Nests on moorlands but winters on estuaries and often on rocky coasts.

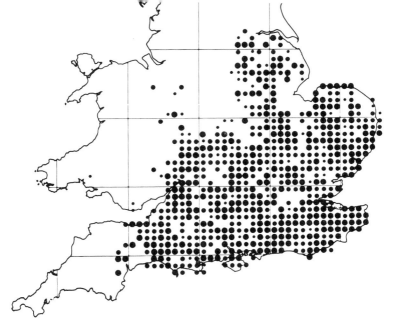

This is a detail of the Nightingale distribution map from the *Atlas of Breeding Birds of Britain and Ireland* to which 10,000 birdwatchers contributed through the BTO.

will only mention one or two here. The Reader's Digest *Book of British Birds* published by Drive Publications is very comprehensive and readable even when dealing with quite complex subjects. The third section of the book is a particularly good survey, with lots of very specific illustrations, of the biology and behaviour of birds.

In *Birds*, one of the Countryside Series published by Collins, Dr Christopher Perrins writes about the ways in which birds adapt to their environment. The book begins with a chapter on natural selection and evolution and goes on to describe adaptions for feeding, breeding, winter survival and migration as well as having sections on changes in numbers and the effect of changes in the environment.

Finally, in this short list I would include *The Atlas of Breeding Birds in Britain and Ireland*, compiled by Dr J. T. R. Sharrock for the British Trust for Ornithology and the Irish Wildbird Conservancy and published by Poyser. The book shows the precise distribution of 219 breeding birds of Britain and Ireland. The accompanying text describes the bird's habitat and gives an historical background to the present distribution and population size. It is a fascinating book which you can always pick up and find something interesting to read about.

Journals Because birdwatching is so popular both as a form of recreation and as a science and can be practised by amateurs as well as professionals several journals are published, each with a slightly different editorial policy.

Birds is published quarterly by the RSPB and sent to its members free of charge. This is a very popular magazine which contains a wide variety of articles on birds, both common and rare, bird protection, behaviour and biology as well as news of RSPB and other ornithological events. It is liberally illustrated with colour photographs and paintings and is really in a field of its own.

Bird Study is the quarterly journal of the British Trust for Ornithology and is sent free to members. It publishes the results of corporate research organized by the Trust as well as original papers by BTO members of a more general nature. This journal is read by both the keen amateur ornithologist and the scientist.

British Birds is a monthly magazine devoted to British birds published by Macmillan Journals Ltd. This journal is, again, read by both the keen amateur ornithologist and scientist. Like *Bird Study* it is a journal that one keeps and forms the basis of a library. It publishes original observations in the form of scientific papers or short notes. Also included are reviews and comments; the journal is also illustrated with excellent black and white photographs.

Ibis is the quarterly journal of the British Ornithologists' Union and publishes papers on birds and ornithology anywhere in the world. It is a valuable and uncompromisingly scientific journal for the ornithologist.

I am not suggesting that you should purchase all these journals or indeed that they are all the journals that an ornithologist will look at in the course of a year. A more comprehensive list can be found in appendix I. *Ringing and Migration* and *Wildfowl* cover more specific areas than the previous journals, while the *Journal of Animal Ecology*, the *Journal of Applied Ecology*, the *Journal of Zoology* and *Behaviour* all carry some scientific papers about birds. Your local 'bird club' may take copies of these journals. It is also possible for the serious student to make use of the libraries of the Edward Grey Institute for Field Ornithology at Oxford, the RSPB, the BTO at Tring, the Scottish Ornithologists' Club in Edinburgh and the British Museum (Natural History).

At this point I should mention three excellent regional journals. In Scotland the Scottish Ornithologists' Club publishes *Scottish Birds* which includes notes and articles on Scottish Ornithology. In Wales, *Nature in Wales* published by the Naturalists' Trusts of Wales, includes the ornithological report for Wales as well as other papers on birds and other aspects of natural history in Wales. In Ireland the Irish Wildbird Conservancy publishes the *IWC News*. At a local level the county birds clubs annually publish county bird reports which are the results of observations and surveys by local members and represent much of the work which is undertaken by these clubs. These reports represent the basic data

National surveys which result in such works as the *Breeding Birds of Britain and Ireland* are often based on the county bird clubs' annual reports.

from which it is possible to detect the fluctuations in the populations of birds over the years. It is usually from these sources too, that the county bird books are compiled.

Sound guides One of the great delights of birdwatching are the sweet and varied songs and calls that some birds can produce whether it is simply the song of a Robin or the raucous chorus of seabirds on their cliffs or the murmur of thousands of ducks as they loaf and feed on some undisturbed lake. Since every species has its individual vocabulary, your ability to identify a bird's song and its calls can add greatly to your efficiency as a birdwatcher.

There are a number of recordings on the market either on record or cassette tape. A set of these recordings is most useful in early spring for reminding you of the songs and calls of the summer visitors, particularly the ones which are so difficult to differentiate, like the Garden Warbler and the Blackcap or the Sedge and Reed Warblers. Some of the best recordings are to be found in the following records or cassettes.

The BBC have produced a whole range of discs and cassettes, some mono and others stereo, of a wide range of wildlife recordings including a twelve-inch disc *British Wild Birds in Stereo*. Also available is *Woodland and Garden Birds* which can be bought on two cassettes or mono discs.

Bird Concerts, produced by the Roché Institute, consists of recordings of birds of different habitats from various parts of the world. They make a very useful series for the traveller-birdwatcher. The *Shell Nature Series* consists of nine records of over one hundred species of birds and is arranged according to habitat. Finally there are two less pretentious recordings which are worth considering. Richard Margoschis has just produced a stereo cassette entitled *British Wildlife Habitats No 1* with natural sounds from eight different habitats; and *Wildlife Sound Tracks* on eight cassettes is recorded and privately published by John Kirby, 10 Wycherley Avenue, Middlesborough, Cleveland.

How to meet people Unless you are a complete 'loner' you can increase your enjoyment of birdwatching by joining one of the bird societies, clubs, or RSPB members' groups which exist in most counties. In some heavily populated areas there may be a bird club or RSPB members' group in every town. The main function of such clubs is to stimulate an interest in the birds of that county by means of lectures, field excursions and regular bulletins of recently recorded birds. Most importantly they survey annually the county status of each species, the results of which are published in an annual bird report. These local clubs may help with nationally based surveys such as those organized by the BTO. Joining such a club is well worthwhile as it allows you to meet others who are interested in birdwatching and also gives you the opportunity to contribute to the work of the club.

The Royal Society for the Protection of Birds is the largest society of its kind in the country, if not in the world, with over a quarter of a million members. Its chief function is to ensure the better protection of wild birds and to create a public awareness in birds and their place in nature. Its reserves protect almost 40,000 hectares of bird habitat which can be visited daily and also require voluntary help from people who are prepared to spend a week or so wardening and helping with the general management of the reserves. Involvement by its members in local groups has grown enormously in recent years with the idea of drawing members together and arranging lectures and excursions as well as fund-raising activities. Every year the RSPB holds an annual conference attended by large numbers of its members. Whether you are a 'bird-lover' or an expert ornithologist you ought to belong to the RSPB.

Once you have passed through the early stages of identifying birds and have become interested in asking and answering questions about birds and joining others to help answer those questions you should join the British Trust for Ornithology. This national organization apart from stimulating and organizing a lot of very useful field research has three conferences a year which can be well worth attending.

Identification

In the last chapter I have described the various aids which may help you to watch birds and enable you to become one of the 'curious naturalists', to use the title of one of Niko Tinbergen's books. To pursue these aims you need to give the birds their correct names; only when you can do this can you talk about them with others and read up about them. Identification is not simple. There is no point in using incorrect names, and if you do, you will not fool anyone for very long. The discipline needed in order to identify correctly a bird teaches you to be observant, accurate in your descriptions and dispassionate and discriminating in your conclusions. Like many subjects you may wish to study there are few, if any, short cuts through the hard grind of memorizing colours, shapes, songs and field marks.

A birdwatching friend can help you through some initial stages by taking you to different habitats; he can open your eyes and teach you how to search for birds and indicate their field marks and other important attributes.

You will also be helped by joining one of the trips organized by your local bird club. In this way you can often visit a number of good birding places fairly cheaply and have the benefit of a multitude of eyes spotting the birds.

All your life you can continue to learn more about the finer points of identification. You will always be seeing birds in new places, hearing unusual call-notes or seeing them in quite extraordinary postures which may for a time, completely fool you. If you are lucky enough to travel to other parts of the world you may meet completely new families of birds and therefore have to learn to identify them from scratch.

When you start learning to identify birds it is best to use one of the field guides with a limited number of species. This reduces the chance of you confusing, say, a common garden bird with a rare visitor from abroad. Having obtained a guide turn to the chapter which tells you how to use the book as first you must learn something of the topography of the bird's feathers before you can properly understand the descriptions of the birds themselves or write your own field descriptions. In the illustration below you will find the usual names of the different feathers, including those of the upper and undersides of the bird's wing. Names such as scapulars and axillaries appear rather daunting at first but most of them are used fairly regularly amongst birdwatchers.

Many warblers, waders and other species have eye and supercilary stripes of various lengths, colours and thicknesses. It has been suggested that they help the bird to aim its beak at a particle of food. The edge of the

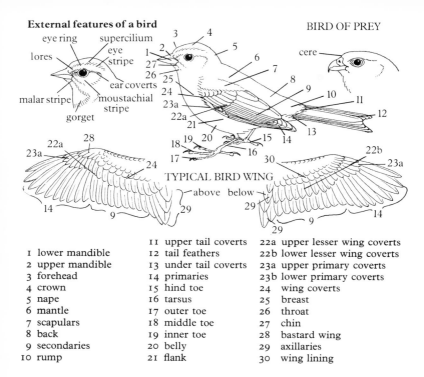

External features of a bird

BIRD OF PREY

eye ring
supercilium
lores
eye
stripe
ear coverts
malar stripe
moustachial
stripe
gorget

cere

TYPICAL BIRD WING

above   below

1 lower mandible	11 upper tail coverts	22a upper lesser wing coverts
2 upper mandible	12 tail feathers	22b lower lesser wing coverts
3 forehead	13 under tail coverts	23a upper primary coverts
4 crown	14 primaries	23b lower primary coverts
5 nape	15 hind toe	24 wing coverts
6 mantle	16 tarsus	25 breast
7 scapulars	17 outer toe	26 throat
8 back	18 middle toe	27 chin
9 secondaries	19 inner toe	28 bastard wing
10 rump	20 belly	29 axillaries
	21 flank	30 wing lining

black cap of many species may have the same effect. Another part of the bird to which particular attention should be paid are the wings and the coverts which are smallish feathers of different shapes and sizes lying over the bases of the primary and secondary flight feathers. You need to know them because they or their tips may be coloured differently from the remainder of the wing and thus produce the wing bars which can be prominent field marks.

Field marks are one of the major aids to identification and are any conspicuous features in a bird's plumage or shape. They can be prominent patches of colour such as the red of a cock Bullfinch's breast, its blue-black cap or its white rump. Other field marks may be the presence of wing bars, white outer tail-feathers or a forked tail or curved bill or indeed anything which is conspicuous. Some may be hidden when the bird is at rest. The Redwing's red flanks can be seen only partially and the Grey Plover's black patch on its axillaries cannot be seen until the bird actually lifts its wings and flies. Another point to watch for is that some colours are not what they seem: for instance, is the colour that you see on the Starling in sunlight the true colour of its feathers or is it due to iridescence? Iridescence is caused by the physical nature of the structure of the barbules which interferes with the normal refraction of light from the feather surface. Adult Starlings, Magpies, Lapwings, and the drakes of several species of wildfowl have this type of plumage. Also remember that the evening sun often casts a red tinge and you can, if you forget this, see some most extraordinary coloured birds. Describing colours is always rather difficult and I try to remember the colour makers' names for artists' colours which are fairly uniform.

A note on size is important in your field description. Field guides usually give the length in centimetres or inches at the beginning of every section. This is generally the measurement of a specimen placed flat on its back and taken from the tip of its beak to the end of its tail. As you do not usually see a bird in the field like this, it is better to try and compare the size with another species known to you. The size of flying birds is notoriously difficult to judge; a prisoner-of-war friend of mine used to illustrate this problem with a story that one day he and a friend were lying on a bank chatting and idly watching a Kestrel hovering on the other side of the bank. After a time the Kestrel changed the direction of its flight and turned out to be a Red Admiral butterfly which had been in difficulty flying up into the wind and it only became recognizable when it moved off in another direction.

Shape is a give-away feature in many species. Is, for instance, the body of the bird you have seen, tubby and upright like a Robin or slim and horizontal like a Wagtail? Is it long-legged? Does it have a long neck or a long tail? As you become more experienced you will get to know many birds by their shape. You will obviously be able to tell that a certain bird is a duck but you will also be able to tell a Wigeon by its pronounced forehead or a Pintail by its long thin neck and needle-like tail. You will also be able to distinguish the Mallard by its cocked-up tail from the Pochard with its more rounded body and tail that lies almost on the water. Another way of learning bird shapes is to draw them. Drawing birds makes you concentrate on essential details and teaches you to look at them in a different and refreshing way.

Two other factors that need to be taken into account when identifying birds are geographical range and the habitat in which the bird has been found.

If you identify a species which is not normally present in the area in which you are birdwatching it would be wise to re-check your identification and make sure you have an adequate field description and then report your sighting to your county recorder.

A bird's habitat is not really a diagnostic feature as, particularly on migration, birds can turn up in all sorts of places, but it can be an indication. For example, if you find a yellowish-bellied wagtail on a water meadow in south-east England it is more likely to be a Yellow Wagtail than a Grey Wagtail. In Wales you are more likely to see a Grey Wagtail along rocky streamsides. With large groups of birds such as ducks each species will differ in its choice of habitat. Amongst the ducks, for instance, some prefer saltwater such as the Scoters and Long-tailed Ducks whereas Pochards and

Bird shapes

Grey Heron

Mallard

Kestrel

Lapwing

Woodpigeon

Herring Gull

Tawny Owl

Great Spotted Woodpecker

Whitethroat

Swallow

Swift

Chaffinch

Robin

Tufted Ducks prefer freshwater. Amongst the waders, Purple Sandpipers and Turnstones forage mostly on the seashore whereas a lot of waders may be just as much at home on a freshwater shoreline as in a saline habitat. So not only should you check the distribution maps but you should also look carefully at the description of the species' normal habitat. Some birds are gradually changing their habitat in a rather subtle way. Up to a few years ago, you hardly ever found a Reed Bunting away from the vicinity of water but recently it seems to be spreading over to drier habitats that are more characteristic of the Yellowhammer.

The way a bird moves must be noted and, when considered with the shape, can be a diagnostic feature. Was it walking, one foot down after the other, comparatively slowly, or running with 'twinkling' feet? When searching for food, larger birds usually walk. Large waders like Oystercatchers, Curlews and godwits, as well as Ravens, Rooks, ducks and geese, all tend to walk. Plovers can run for short distances then they stop, look and listen. Smaller waders like the Sanderling 'twinkle' or run with 'twinkling' feet along the edge of the waves while Dunlins twist and turn digging busily and deeply into the wet sand or soft mud. On a lawn the Pied Wagtail may rush around after flying insects; in contrast, Chaffinches are sedate walkers. Blackbirds and Song Thrushes, like most of their family hop or run and hop – the Blackbird when displaying to an intruder and therefore somewhat excited, runs, adopting a rather special posture of the body known as the 'rodent run'.

When you see a flock of small birds feeding amongst the branches, what is their method of locomotion? Do they sidle up the twigs like some of the warblers or hop from branch to branch or twig to twig like the tits? On tree trunks, two or three species may hunt together – how do they climb the tree? Do they circle gradually up the trunk or do they go straight up? Once they have got to the top of one tree how do they get to the bottom of another? The Treecreeper, for instance, rarely climbs down a tree: once it has climbed fairly high it will fly to the bottom of another tree and even to the bottom of the tree it has just climbed, while the Nuthatch can walk down.

Some birds fly in a very distinctive manner. Once you have learnt the regular and deep rounded wing beats of the Lapwing, flashing black and white, you will be able to identify it so long as you can see movement of the wings. The commonest feature to notice is whether the flight is level or undulating: finches, buntings and wagtails all have an undulating flight caused by the bird beating its wings for a second or two and then closing them. Each species has its own flight pattern depending upon the speed and number of wing beats. The Grey Heron flies swiftly and directly across the sky, and its slow wing beats deceive you as to its speed over the ground. Geese fly in lines or in V-shape formations, Woodpigeons in loose flocks,

With experience you will be able to identify families, genera and even some species merely by their shape alone.

Buzzards soar and wheel, Kestrels hover, while Swallows and martins wheel, swirl and chatter over water-meadows and villages.

When you look at water birds, how do they swim? Do they sit high in the water like Geese or low like Shags? How do they dive? Do they slip under the water or jacknife themselves out of the water to gain impetus?

Finally when talking about the different features by which you identify a bird you may hear people saying that it has the 'jizz' of some particular bird. There is nothing magic about the word which was first used, so far as I am aware, by T. A. Coward in the introduction to one of his very popular books on British birds. It is most often used when you can only see the bird imperfectly against the light or amongst vegetation. Your accumulated experience with birds takes into account what little you can see of its shape and in its method of moving, as well as its habitat and comes up with the impression that the bird is whatever you think it has the 'jizz' of.

Song and calls I have nearly always found that songs, calls or other sounds made by birds such as the drumming of woodpeckers or Snipe are a great help to identification. They are often very distinctive. Indeed, it is easier to separate the Chiffchaff and Willow Warbler, Marsh and Willow Tit by their song rather than relying on a distant view. On the other hand, the songs of at least two pairs of birds are difficult to separate, they are the Garden Warbler and the Blackcap, which often sing in similar woodland habitats, and also the Sedge and Reed Warblers, in marshes, and if you happen to be on the Continent or even in some parts of western England you may have the Marsh Warbler to add to the confusion. However, with practice it is possible to sort out most of these problems. Each species has its own vocabulary of call notes by which it communicates to other members of its own species, and sometimes with individuals of similar but different species. The calls of closely related species can be very similar and need a lot

These sonagrams show that the Willow Warbler has a greater frequency range and that the pitch of the song descends compared with that of the Chiffchaff. (Sonagrams after Jellis.)

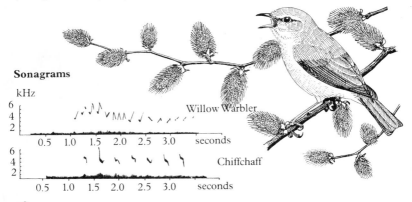

Sonagrams

kHz

Willow Warbler

Chiffchaff

of learning. The communication calls of feeding flocks of tits takes a bit of disentangling as do the 'tacs', 'tecs' and 'tucs' of the Garden Warblers, Blackcaps, Whitethroats, Lesser Whitethroats and a host of other warblers.

Like everything else, you learn the song by listening to a strange call in the field, then tracking down the unknown singer and identifying it visually. There is nothing like the frustration of hearing an invisible bird singing to imprint that song on your memory. A friend may open your ears to a song but should not tell you what it is until you have tried to identify it for yourself. I learnt bird song the hard way by tracking down the singer. However, records or tapes can refresh your memory of songs that you used to identify during the previous year but which, after a winter, are a slightly rusty memory.

I also need to write down from time to time a description of the calls or songs. However, as the voice production of a bird is so very different from our own, the phonetic alphabet we use is only of limited use for this purpose. The specialist in bird song plays his recordings through a piece of special equipment which allows a sound spectogram or sonagram to be produced. These are graphs which show the length of time the call has taken, the tone, the pitch and to some extent the loudness of the call. Although the sonagram will only give you an approximate idea of the sound it can tell experts more about bird song than any other method.

Usually the average birdwatcher who wishes to remind himself or tell someone else what the voice of some bird sounded like has to rely upon a system which tries to link bird sound to some form of phonetic alphabet. Although several attempts have been made to produce a suitable phonetic alphabet none has been satisfactory so far. The task is made difficult by the variety of ways in which birds produce sounds and also by the varying abilities of the listener to hear and record the sounds. These problems are discussed more fully by E. M. Nicholson in an essay on 'Voice' in the new *Handbook of the Birds of Europe, the Middle East and North Africa.* Whilst pointing out the pitfalls and lack of detailed research into this problem he points out that the vowel sounds used in Pitman's shorthand, provides a simple but functional system. In her excellent book, *Bird Sounds and their Meaning*, Rosemary Jellis also emphasises how necessary it is to have a system of sound notation for learning new songs and calls. She gives various guidelines to help construct such a system. For example symbols for 'non-musical' elements and rhythmic patterns are suggested, i.e. a vertical line, as on a sonagram, represents a 'click' and an 'X' represents a single noisy or harsh element in the song or call. Musical notation is adopted to denote rhythm. Anyone who is interested in this field should read both this book and E. M. Nicholson's essay in the *Handbook.*

Some noises produced by birds are not vocalizations at all, for instance, the drumming of the Great and Lesser Spotted Woodpecker when they hammer with their bills on an especially selected piece of a tree, or the drumming of a Snipe as it flies over its breeding habitat, climbing and diving with its tail fanned in such a way that the air rushes past the outer tail feather to produce the bleating sound. In spring the Lapwing when flying over its territory, can, with an especially hard downward thrust of its wings, which forces the air through the wing feathers, create a regular low-pitched vibrant sound. The 'wing-music' of the Mute Swan is well known to all who have been standing round the edge of a lake as a pair has flown past.

The sounds of birds are immensely varied and describing them adequately is a problem. Some like Chiffchaffs, the tits, Yellowhammers and so on, have phrases for which it is relatively simple to produce an alliteration. Others like Blackbirds, Skylarks and warblers, have songs which we now know from the sound spectogram are composed of a series of phrases which may be put together by the singer as it pleases. Other 'songs' are so explosive or guttural that it is virtually impossible to reproduce them in a written form.

Names of birds So far when I have referred to a bird I have given it its English name, but I have not explained what a 'species' is or indeed the need for Latin or scientific names. As birdwatchers, we are chiefly interested in species, whether it is a Robin, which has the Latin or scientific name of *Erithacus rubecula*, or a Great Tit with its scientific name *Parus major*. A species is a population or group which can interbreed and produce fertile offspring. If a member of one species attempted to breed with a member of another species it would generally fail unless the two species were very closely related; if they did suceed in mating then any offspring they produced would be infertile. The species is something real. It is a definite biological unit, which is committed to its own line of evolution.

A species may have exactly the same characteristics throughout the whole of its geographical range or it may consist of populations which vary in appearance, size, song and even habitat. An example of the first group, known as monotypic, is the Osprey, which has a worldwide distribution.

The Osprey is an example of a monotypic species with a world-wide distribution throughout which the characteristics of the species remain constant.

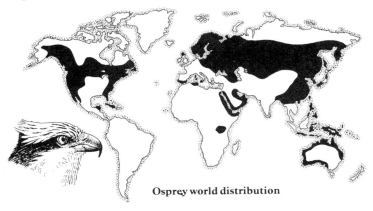

Osprey world distribution

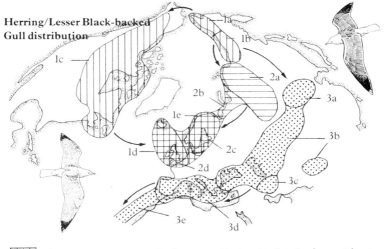

Herring/Lesser Black-backed Gull distribution

	Larus argentatus group: 1a *L. a. vegae* 1b *L. a. birulaii* 1c *L. a. smithsonianu.*
(Herring Gull)	1d *L. a. argentatus* 1e *L. a. omissus*

	Larus fuscus group: 2a *L. f. heuglini* 2b *L. f. antellus* 2c *L. f. fuscus*
(Lesser Black-backed Gull)	2d *L. f. graellsi*

	Larus argentatus or: 3a *L. a.(f). mongolicus* 3b *L. a.(f). cachinnans*
fuscus group	3c *L. a.(f). armenicus* 3d *L. a.(f). michahellis*
	3e *L. a.(f). atlantis*

The Herring Gull is a holarctic species with interlinking geographical races each exhibiting slightly different plumage colours. In northern Europe the two ends of the chain overlap but are now separate species and rarely interbreed.

The other group, with slightly differing populations, is known as polytypic. Sometimes these populations become sufficiently distinct from other groups of the same species that they are known as geographical races or subspecies, which, should they meet and interbreed could still produce fertile offspring. If, however, the populations remain isolated for a sufficiently long period, they might develop in such a way that they can no longer produce fertile offspring and can, therefore, be regarded as distinct species. One of the best examples of a polytypic species whose 'end-forms' are now distinct species is provided by the Herring Gull. If you follow the different races of the Herring Gull from western Europe round the globe through northern Africa, north-east Russia and back to Europe you will find that there is a gradual and continuous change. Finally in Europe the two forms overlap, and the second form is known to us as the Lesser Black-backed Gull. Herring Gulls no longer generally interbreed with Lesser Black-backed Gulls or, if they do, they do not usually produce fertile offspring. Both species nest on the Pembrokeshire island of Skokholm, where I was warden for seven years, and occupy different parts of the island, the Herring Gull nesting on the cliff face and the Lesser Black-backed Gull on the plateau area of the island. Furthermore, the courtship of the two species has in the course of time changed sufficiently so that it is difficult for the two species to interbreed, and they are not only isolated by habitat but, by and large, reproductively isolated too. The Lesser Black-backed Gull is migratory while the Herring Gull is not. This story of the two gulls is a very good example of how geographical isolation – or perhaps distance isolation – can lead to the formation of new species. In this case, each step in the change of the characteristics was so distinct as to be regarded as a race or subspecies. Where finally they overlapped they were geographically, ecologically and to some extent reproductively isolated.

In other cases the changes of colour or size may be very gradual and no distinct step is recognizable; this sort of graduation is known as a 'cline'. The best known example of this is shown by the Guillemot. Some of these birds have a white ring round the eye with a white line over the ear coverts. This mark looks rather like a pair of spectacles and the birds which have this mark are known as bridled Guillemots. The interesting point is that the more northerly population of Guillemots has a higher percentage of bridled forms than those in the south of England. Mr H. N. Southern has organized three surveys at roughly ten-year intervals to discover the percentage of bridled Guillemots in the populations in different parts of the British Isles. While the percentages have changed slightly over the years Southern's figures have shown that less than 1% are bridled in the south of England, 26% are bridled in Shetland, 34% in the Faeroes and $50–70\%$ are bridled in southern Iceland.

The species, then, is a distinct biological unit. Taxonomists have grouped together the species which they think have similar appearances and characteristics into what are known as 'genera' but this grouping is purely subjective.

Linnaeus, a Swedish zoologist, devized a system of naming animals in his *Systema Naturae* in 1758. It is known as the binomial system, every species is placed in a genus and the scientific name of the species thereafter consists both of the generic and the specific names. Hence when I refer to the scientific name of the Blackbird and Song Thrush as *Turdus merula* and *Turdus philomelus* I am also indicating that those birds have been put in the same genus, *Turdus*, with the specific names of *merula* and *philomelus*.

It so happens that when studying evolution, systematists wish to give names to the geographical races that I have mentioned earlier in relation to the Herring Gull and Lesser Black-backed Gull. They have in fact gone one stage further and produced the trinomial system. The generic and specific names remain the same but the subspecies is given a third name. The Herring Gull, for instance, which occurs in Britain is *Larus argentatus argentatus*, whereas the subspecies which occurs in the United States is *Larus argentatus smithsonianus*. A word of warning: the identification of geographical races in the field is very difficult.

Above the level of species and genus again taxonomists tend to differ over

Two of the Guillemots in the picture are the 'bridled' form with their white 'spectacles'; these have been found to be more common in the more northerly colonies.

certain points. There are many divisions and sub-divisions, but here I will only mention three: family, order and class. A family is a grouping of genera which taxonomists expect to have evolved from the same parent stem. For instance, the family Fringilladae includes not only finches like the Chaffinch and Linnet but also the Crossbill. An order is a much broader division within the class. The aim of an order is to express the relationship between families of a similar origin. The families Corvidae (crows), Paridae (tits) and Emberizidae (buntings) are all part of the order Passeriformes. However, some of the relationships are not always clear and are in dispute. Finally, all birds belong to the class Aves.

Nowadays, most lists of birds are set out in what is known as the Wetmore Order, named after the American zoologist Dr Alexander Wetmore who published his proposals in 1960. In making lists of birds for identification books and field guides it is usual to begin with what are believed to be the most primitive forms of birds and work towards the most highly developed. However, it must be realized that all orders listed in this form have no certainty and it is difficult to express any linear relationship between birds. Professor K. H. Voous has just published a *List of recent holarctic bird species* (roughly that part of the globe north of the Tropic of Cancer), and this will no doubt be the standard list for some time to come and has been followed by the editors of the *Handbook of the Birds of Britain, Europe and North Africa*. For the person who is not concerned about taxonomy there is a growing tendency to list birds within their genera in the alphabetical order of their specific names.

43

In the field

I have emphasized that if you want to get close to birds or if you want them to come close to you, you must behave like a hunter but without his desire to kill. Your subdued clothing will disguise you, and a peaked or brimmed hat will hide the paleness of your face. Thus equipped, you must match your clothing. When you move, your actions should be slow and quiet. If you are with a companion it is best not to talk but if you must, it is better to keep a low voice rather than whisper as sibilant sounds often carry well. When moving, it is best to keep your arms still and, even when you bring your binoculars up to your eyes, be patient and slow if possible, because a hasty movement will disturb what you are looking at. If the bird has already flown or has already seen you and is flying away then you must move fast, remembering, however, that you may disturb something else. The clothes you have chosen should be made of a material that does not rustle as you move about. When walking through a wood avoid treading on sticks that will snap noisily. Old twigs will not always snap if you put your weight on them gently. The quiet approach and then a wait in cover giving a reasonable view may give the best results. If you let the birds treat you as part of the scenery they will come closer.

It is a good idea to arrange your binoculars and field notebook in such a position that they can be used without too much movement. If you are in a wood you should sit or stand with your back to a tree or behind a thinly-leaved bush which can be seen through – it is better to look through such a bush than over the top. If you are on open ground and intend to use a low hedge or bush for cover never look over the top but try to look through them or creep slowly round to the front – hopefully your clothes will blend in sufficiently for the birds not to notice you. If you are walking along the top of a sea or river wall you will be outlined starkly against the sky and will frighten the shy waterfowl and waders for a good distance around. It is better to walk along the wall bottom, which unfortunately is often muddy, and crawl up the bank on your belly and peer carefully between the stems of tall plants along the top. However, if this alternative appears rather daunting, walking along the 'bird-side' of the bank is better than along the top.

Try to make use of any cover as you approach the bird, remembering that if you can see the birds they can see you. If you are careful and cunning you may be able to deceive them for a time but watch their reactions as you approach; ducks' heads may go up to watch you, the nearest may fly away

Above The slow beats of the Lapwing and its rounded black and white wings are unmistakable and a distant flock in the evening light seems to be emitting a pulsating white light.

Below The Grey Wagtail is the typical wagtail of the upland streams in the British Isles. On water meadows in the lowlands its place is taken by the Yellow Wagtail.

Left The experienced birdwatcher discovers birds quickly because he knows the shapes to look for, and it is probably by looking for bird shapes that you will discover two cryptically coloured Nightjars in the centre of this picture (and perhaps a third in the foreground).
Right A woodland habitat can shelter large numbers of birds in the different stratas of vegetation. It is a difficult area to census and usually sample areas are chosen.
Below The largest seabird colonies tend to be in the north where there is abundant fish and where differential erosion has created masses of ledges from horizontal bedding planes of sedimentary rocks.

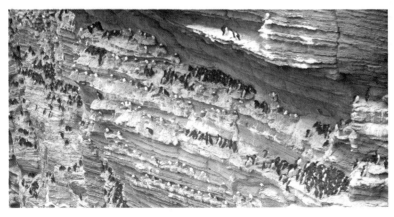

Above When a bird, like this immature Gannet, is landing the wings are brought forward in a braking action and the primaries are bent back by the resistance of the air. Feet also help with the braking action.

Below The Goldfinch is adapted to extracting the seeds of composite plants from their corollas. Its short legs enable it to hang on to precarious perches and its thin bill enables it to probe into tube-like flowers.

This birdwatcher, wearing naturally coloured clothes, is looking through cover. However, even here his white hands may give him away.

and take others with them. If they are satisfied that you present no danger, they will drop their heads and go on feeding or loafing. If you want to try a second approach remember that the birds will already be aware of your presence and therefore much more alert. Small waders may not show much head movement and may simply run ahead of you when you come too close. In many small birds the first sign of anxiety is shown by raising the head, moving the wings out of the breast feathers and an increase in the rate of calling.

Field behaviour Field behaviour is one aspect of birdwatching in which some people can be rather weak. Two points must always be remembered: firstly, most land, even the foreshore, belongs to someone; secondly, it is important to show a deep concern for the welfare of the birds. Unless you happen to know that a landowner does not object to the public entering his land such as, for instance, the Crown Commissioners who are responsible for the foreshore, you should get permission to enter.

Rights of way throughout the country are very good when local authorities keep them clear, and they enable people to pass and repass through a wide variety of private lands. A map showing rights of way can usually be seen at the County Surveyor's office. You can copy them onto your own Ordnance Survey map as the paths shown on this are not necessarily rights of way.

A number of different codes of conduct have been drawn up for people visiting the country. Most elements of the codes are common sense but it does us all good periodically to think whether in one respect or another we have been thoughtless and so I will repeat here the Countryside Commission's Country Code:—*Guard against all fire risks. Fasten all gates. Keep dogs under proper control. Keep to paths across farmland. Avoid damage to fences, hedges and walls. Leave no litter. Safeguard water supplies. Protect wildlife, wild plants and trees. Go carefully on country roads. Respect the life of the country.* The warning to respect the life of the country is needed, particularly in relation to trespass and sometimes in relation to damage to private property. Also, there have been a number of instances where rare birds have been harried by over-keen listers who have put their own private gratification before the welfare of the bird.

The Protection of Birds Acts 1954–67 are really codes of conduct for all those who are interested in birds. The theme of the Acts are that all wild birds and their nests and eggs are protected. Anything which physically harms them or their nests, eggs or young is forbidden. Some species which are particularly endangered in this country are given special protection, and if anyone commits an offence in respect of them, they are liable to penalties of up to £100 for each offence. For offences against commoner birds they are liable to maximum fines of £25. Game birds like some of the ducks, pheasants and partridges may be shot in the open season which usually begins in the early autumn and ends before birds begin breeding. There is evidence that certain species like Woodpigeons, House Sparrows and even the beautiful Bullfinches, in the south-east of England, can be pests and a section in the Acts allows authorized people to shoot these species and others listed on the Second Schedule to the Acts.

The birdwatcher has to be particularly careful about disturbance to rare birds listed on the First Schedule to the Acts. A section in the 1967 Act made the wilful disturbance of wildbirds listed in this Schedule while they are near an occupied nest an offence liable to a special penalty. This has led to some rather peculiar situations in places like Shetland where birds such as Whimbrels, which are in the First Schedule, are very common and where it is virtually impossible to walk over certain moors without wilfully disturbing them. Theoretically, while the botanist or the shepherd may walk across these moors because they do not recognize the alarm calls of the Whimbrel, the conscientious birdwatcher hearing the calls should leave the area as soon as possible. However, the principle behind this particular law is important and is to some extent covered by the *Birdwatcher's Code*. If you should wish to disturb one of these First Schedule birds for scientific purposes, or to photograph or ring them, you should obtain the approval of the Nature Conservancy Council. In the case of ringing or nest recording permission can be obtained through the BTO. The RSPB will send you a copy of their leaflet *Wild Birds and the Law* free of charge if you send them a stamped addressed envelope.

The importation of various species of birds is forbidden under the Protection of Birds Act. More recently Parliament has enacted the Endangered Species (Import and Export) Act 1976 which has the effect of implementing some form of control over the import and export of some of the rarest animals, and plants of Britain and the world. For instance, the falcons, such as the Peregrine Falcon, are listed in the First Schedule, which means that anyone wishing to import one must not only obtain a licence from the country into which he wishes to import the bird but also an export licence from the country of origin. This procedure gives the Scientific Authority of both countries a chance to assess the status of the bird and whether its export or import will be harmful to its native population.

The RSPB's *Birdwatcher's Code* begins with the words: 'The welfare of the birds and its nest should be your first consideration', and this thought should be with you all the time. The BTO produces at least two codes of conduct, one for ringing and one for those who take part in its nest record scheme. The RSPB and the Zoological Photographic Society has published a code of conduct for bird photographers. Each code emphasizes that 'the bird's interest must come first' and then deals with the more practical damage that carelessness on the part of people ringing, nest recording or photographing can do.

A bird's nest is one of the most sensitive places in its life and it is the centre of attraction for many birdwatchers. Some may wish to find nests because they enjoy the search. Others will be recording data for the nest record scheme of the BTO. Bird ringers want to find nests because they wish to ring young so that they may later be able to age the birds more exactly and so follow its life through. Some may be carrying out life-history studies and the nest is where life begins. There are other people who still collect birds' eggs even though it has long been forbidden by law. Only seldomly are they collected for any good scientific reasons. Constant examination of the nest can also put it at risk either by causing the bird to desert or by destroying the natural cover or even by making a track to the nest, which predators can easily follow.

The point about codes and laws is that they spell out certain rules for those who have no real feeling for the countryside nor for the creatures that live in it. To the real naturalist who has a feeling or a love for the countryside the ethic comes naturally.

Where to see birds Birds can be found everywhere from city centres and industrial areas to the most luxuriant and ancient woodlands and reedy marshlands. Some can be very obvious like the Blackbirds and Robins in your garden, although both can be very inconspicuous at some times of the year when in woodlands. Some warblers skulk in the bottoms of bushes and reedbeds, occasionally calling to each other, keeping an eye on you, but at the same time being extremely difficult to see. The phrase, 'keeping an eye on you' is a very telling one because when you do manage to catch a sight of the bird it is often the eye that you see, peering at you through some gap in the foliage. Quite a number of birds play hide and seek with you in this way: the Great Spotted Woodpecker hides its body and peers out from behind a tree, while the Wheatear peers over the top of a rock.

Although birds live in almost every habitat the problem is often to find them. The beginner will have difficulty in picking out the same number of birds as the experienced birdwatcher and will wonder at the latter's quickness, which can be despairing at times. Improving the sharpness of your eye is a matter of continual practice. By all means start out with an expert, who will pick out the bird for you, pointing out its shape as it preens or hunts against its natural background. What you are really trying to do at this stage is to learn the shape of all the different species you are likely to see, to learn the 'bird image' in a wide variety of backgrounds, so that you will not think for long that a knob on the branch of a gnarled old tree, or that an oddly shaped tuft of grass on the meadow or a rock on a hillside, is really a bird. Like almost everything else continual practice at searching will bring you the acuity to pick up quickly the 'bird image' whether it is stationary or moving.

How you look at birds will depend to some extent on whether you are walking through the countryside or just sitting quietly. If you are walking and you see a bird with your naked eye that needs identifying you will stop and look at it through your binoculars. However, if you choose a reasonably comfortable position and sit still preferably with the light and some cover behind you, you can sweep large vistas. If you are facing open ground, you can count Lapwings and Golden Plovers, or check the edge of a reed marsh for Herons, Coots and Moorhens or even the stealthy emergence of a Bittern. If you are by an estuary such a position is ideal for counting ducks and waders.

There are many exciting habitats throughout the British Isles and abroad but a birdwatcher-naturalist will find, in the long run, that his own 'patch' provides the most rewarding field of discovery. Although I had a birdwatching 'patch' when I was confined in a POW camp in Germany, and when I was a warden of the exciting island of Skokholm for seven years, I really only learned to work my area thoroughly when I was doing field work for the BTO's Bird Atlas Project. I live in the western part of Cambridgeshire, which could be considered very dull ornithologically as it has none of the exciting fenland habitats being mostly agricultural land with few hedges, but with some quite interesting woods. However, during this field work I got to know virtually every habitat within my ten kilometre square including every path, stream and wood, and, I hope, became

RSPB reserves

Ramna Stacks • ⬝ Fetlar

Noup Cliffs •
North Hill
Papa Westray
Marwick
Head •
⬝ Copinsay
Hobbister •
Birsay Moors
and Cottasgarth

Handa •

Culbin Sands •
⬝ Loch of Strathbeg

Balranald •
Loch Garten •
Insh Marshes •
Fowlsheugh

Loch of Kinnordy •
Vane Farm •
Skinflats •
⬝ Forth Islands
Lochwinnoch •
Inchmickery
Horse Island

Rathlin Island •
Cliffs
⬝ Coquet Island

Swan Island •
Shanes Castle •
⬝ Cowpen Marsh
Castle Caldwell •
Mull of Galloway •
St Bees Head •

Leighton Moss •
and Morecambe Bay
Bempton Cliffs •
Green and •
Blockhouse Islands
Blacktoft Sands •
Hornsea Mere

South Stack •
Cliffs
Fairburn Ings •
Tetney Marshes •
Ynys Fenrig
⬝ East Wood
Titchwell •

Lake Vyrnwy •
Coombes Valley •
Snettisham •
Ynys-hir •
Ouse Washes •
Strumpshaw Fen •
The Lodge
and Sutton Fen
Minsmere •
North Warren
Gwenffrwd and Dinas •
Fowlmere
Wolves Wood •
Nagshead •
Rye House Marsh
Haverga...
Island
Grassholm •
Church Wood •
Northward Hill •
Elmley Marshes •

Chapel Wood •
Barfold Copse •
⬝ Dungeness
Arne •
Forewood
Radipole Lake •

The RSPB protects bird communities in a wide variety of habitats which are
managed on scientific advice to provide the optimum conditions for birds.

A view across the valley of the Doethie to the Sessile Oak woods of the RSPB's reserve at the Gwenffryd where Pied Flycatchers, Redstarts and Wood Warblers nest. Kites may occasionally forage over the sheep walks.

familiar with the various species which bred there.

Even living in towns is not a bar to birdwatching and many birdwatchers spend their weekends studying the distribution of birds in the parks and squares. London itself, particularly the area included in Greater London, has some remarkably good birdwatching areas in which much research has been done. The London Natural History Society like many of its kind has a good ornithological section and some of the results of the research are published in its journal the *London Naturalist*. *The Atlas of Breeding Birds of the London Area* edited by David Montier is also very helpful.

Should you require a change from your own area or, perhaps, when you are on holiday, you will wish to know the best places to look for birds. John Gooders' *Where to Watch Birds* will help you in Britain. This book, as well as giving general guidance, pinpoints reserves, and tells you whether permits are needed.

Many of the reserves in this country belong either to the Government's Nature Conservancy Council or to voluntary conservation bodies, particularly the County Naturalists' Trusts, the National Trust, the RSPB, the Society for the Promotion of Nature Conservation, the Wildfowl Trust and a few enterprising local bird clubs. If you would like to visit the reserves of these organizations you should contact them enclosing a stamped addressed envelope and they will send you the necessary information concerning permits, arrangements, etc. The RSPB, for instance, produces annually details of the arrangements to visit its superb range of reserves, covering most habitat types.

While most of the properties owned by the organizations are areas of natural or semi-natural vegetation, the Wildfowl Trust specializes in collections of birds. At Slimbridge, Gloucestershire and Peakirk, Northamptonshire, you can see captive wildfowl at close quarters under very good conditions, which may help you solve identification problems. It has also recently been acquiring land as wildfowl refuges where waterfowl may be seen under much wilder conditions.

Your enjoyment of birds on your visits to these areas may be limited to just identifying and listing the birds you have seen. However, my pleasure has been much increased if I have been able to write up a fairly complete description of what I have seen on the visit. From geological maps you can discover the nature of the underlying rock and perhaps details about the soil. A description of the vegetation including the trees, the shrubs and the herb layer, as well as the amount of water present, is useful. You could also use the sort of habitat check-list that I mention in chapter eleven. This will complement your notes on the bird life and if nothing else the complete description will be much more interesting if you return in later years. If you visit the place regularly over the years your notes may provide a basis for a history of vegetation and bird population changes.

When to see birds Birds are present in almost any type of habitat throughout the year. Seasonally, their abundance may well vary and these changes should be of interest to the birdwatcher-naturalist. He will want to know why birds are absent or why there has been a change, so even an empty habitat is not devoid of interest. In the 'bird-year' the seasons seem to merge imperceptively into each other. For instance, spring, for me begins in March but many birds have already established their nesting territories. Our familiar Robin, for example, has probably been singing since January or even late December. Early spring is a good time to search for birds as the swelling leaf buds do not yet make an effective barrier. It is now that you should watch out for the first Chiffchaffs, while they search continuously for early insects amongst the taller deciduous trees. On the days immediately after their arrival they will sing a quiet subsong which is very different from their usual song which for many birdwatchers is the first sign that our summer migrants are on their way. Shortly after the arrival of the Chiffchaff, the Willow Warbler can be heard sometimes singing in the same trees as the former bird, but also from the lower shrub layer.

On the coastal cliffs and shingle banks and the bare heavily grazed links and dunes, the first Wheatears will have begun to appear. Arriving earliest on the westernmost peninsulas of Cornwall and Wales, they seem to penetrate through to the eastern parts of England a week or so later. In Pembrokeshire the first large influx appears to average about the 29th of March, although the first birds might have arrived three weeks earlier.

Along the laneside hedges and gardens birds are returning from their winter wandering to nest. By mid-March in my village in Cambridgeshire the first Greenfinches and Linnets are beginning to settle down. These birds are largely absent during the winter, appearing at the bird table only after cold weather or a snowfall. Our Goldfinches, which winter south of Britain, arrive later in April, and nest in the old pear and apple trees which are no longer pruned or sprayed.

On the islands and seabird cliffs the auks come and go. Guillemots may have visited the ledges for brief periods from November onwards and now in late March and early April they have been joined by Razorbills and Puffins and sit, bobbing about, on the sea. Then early one morning the Razorbills and Guillemots paddle rapidly over the water, lift off and circle upwards and in towards the cliffs, landing finally with a thump on their ledges. Usually the Puffins remain on the water until around midday when the two other species are going back to sea again. Suddenly thousands of these clown-like birds will circle up over the clifftops. Some return to the sea again but others alight and either rush at once into a burrow or stand on the sward, waddling around, peering into others' burrows. Masses of them, too, just circle overhead.

In April and May the later migrants arrive and establish their breeding territories. Others are passing on to their breeding grounds further north. Birds seeking shelter for their nests and food for their young gradually return to habitats which have been empty throughout the winter. On the other hand, estuaries which have been teeming with bird-life during the winter months are now empty as there is nowhere for the birds to breed. During June the last of the summer migrants will have arrived and those which have been successful in obtaining mates will be well on with their nesting. By now the young of the first Wheatears to arrive will be leaving their nests and from then on the numbers of young birds launching themselves into the world will be increasing enormously. May and June are wonderful months to travel in Britain whether it is to the mountains and moorlands, or to the sea with its cliffs and islands or to the northern forests and lakes. The island cliffs are beautiful with their huge drifts of Sea Campion, Thrift and the occasional Spring Squill.

As summer creeps up the hills many species of bird such as the Skylark, Meadow Pipit, Wheatear, Curlew and Golden Plover, together with the occasional Dunlin, can be found nesting amongst the heather, rushes, sedge and bog cotton. On the Orkney moors the Arctic Skuas, Common Gulls and even the Great Skua have come to nest.

By mid-June the breeding season has finished for some species. Some of the waders have failed to find mates or have lost their eggs or young and from this time onwards small flocks of Lapwings can be seen dispersing as they fly across England towards Wales, or even Ireland. In the arable counties of England the cereal crop has not been harvested and there are few places for the Lapwing to rest. In Cambridgeshire, the Lapwing numbers build up after the harvest, when the ground has been ploughed or burned. The Curlews also move west, but in much smaller numbers, at this time. The Green Sandpiper appears in smaller numbers still and can be found, interestingly, foraging along the edges of quite small streams and ponds, even in gardens.

In July some of the earlier migrants are already beginning their return journey. The bulk of the Swifts leave after a short breeding season. In the woods the singing has stopped and the thick foliage make birds difficult to find. It is also the time of year when birds are difficult to identify too. Many of the drakes are in eclipse plumage and look like the ducks and as a result of losing their flight feathers are barely able to fly. The juvenile plumages of many like Starlings, Robins and gulls, for example, are sufficiently different from the adult plumage to be confusing.

August is the 'betwixt and between' month, the first half of which is not particularly good for birds. Most of them have finished breeding, the adults are moulting and their young have dispersed from the nesting sites, some are also busy fattening themselves up in readiness for their long and sometimes hazardous journey to their winter quarters. When I was staying on Alderney, in the Channel Islands, I always expected to see a large movement of small warblers from the 20th to the 25th of August. Also in the last half of August such birds as the Dunlin, Turnstone, Ringed Plover, Redshank and Curlew begin to re-appear in large numbers on our shores. Some will move on but a few will be staying with us. This is the season for change: birds are moving from one part of the world to another and from one habitat to another. Some of the most noticeable visible migration is provided by the Swallows moving south along the coast towards the shortest sea crossing in the southeast.

Later in the autumn, the movement can become spectacular when the Swallows are joined by Meadow Pipits, Starlings, Lapwings, Chaffinches and Bramblings, all tending to move in a roughly westerly or south-westerly direction but occasionally being directed away from their main course by some geographical feature. The observation of visible migration has tended to become a little unfashionable because the use of radar techniques has solved so many problems. However, in order to experience the pure thrill of birds, there is nothing like the rush of migrants an hour or so after sunrise on a calm bright morning. Although you can see large numbers migrating in some parts of Britain, the spectacular movements take place on the continent. I can remember watching this in Germany during the war, and later on the shores of the Issjelmeer in the Netherlands, as well as the Pembrokeshire coast. Visible migration has been studied at inland sites in Britain by Dr David Lack, Eric Simms and others. However, it would be very valuable to study it again in many parts of the country, comparing the results of the past surveys with more recent information. Many species migrate at night and radar is needed to detect their direction of flight and the times of the movement. Redwings, Fieldfares and other thrushes which move at night often reveal their presence as they fly over by their calls.

Finally, during winter from December to March, most birds have left their breeding habitats to find the places where food is more abundant. The moorlands and cliffs are now empty while the estuaries are full of birds, and some fields, particularly those that are grazed by sheep, now hold masses of Lapwings and Golden Plover and various species of thrush. Fields, hedges, rick yards and even small wooded villages with mature gardens which have the aspect of rather open woodland, can support large numbers of birds, although the woods themselves hold fewer birds in winter. Strangers from the far north may winter here, such as the Rough-legged Buzzard, the Great Grey Shrike and northern duck like the Smew and Long-tailed Duck appear around our coast.

If the weather should harden and snow and ice come in from the east you may see spectacular foul-weather movements with thousands of birds heading west, and in the west itself you may see them leaving the Pembrokeshire headlands to cross the sea to Ireland.

January and February can be cold and harsh but after the mid-winter solstice the Robin and the Skylark begin to sing again. During the following months they are joined by other hedgerow birds bringing us back to March and the beginning of spring.

The sport of birdwatching Whilst I have been rather denigrating the pursuit of listing birds as the be-all and end-all of birdwatching, it would be wrong never to relax and spend a day just seeing how many birds you can locate. This can be done, limiting yourself to an area, or perhaps a time limit, for example, twenty-four hours, or even a target figure. You must always keep to the birdwatcher's code and the country code remembering particularly that the welfare of the birds and the life of the country must come first.

In one of the commonest of the birdwatching sports a team, usually of four people, sets out to list as many species as possible within twenty-four hours. In the Britsh Isles, to see over one hundred different species within the day is good going. The participants have to travel in the same car. At one point the rules vary: some people say that all members of the team must see each bird recorded and others say that only one of the team needs to see the bird. The necessity to travel in the same car does exert some control over the team's manoeuvrability. The keenest people usually make a reconnaissance a day or so beforehand so that they can locate the areas where some of the less common birds are likely to be on the 'big day'. An early start is made so that any night birds still calling or being noisy can be located. The whole day is spent on the chase. There is a difficult problem to resolve: how much do you rush round from one habitat to another with the hope of picking species typical of the area? It is important to remember the old fisherman's adage: you cannot catch fish if your hook is out of the water, which could be translated as: do not spend too long in the car. In some competitions you are restricted to birdwatching within the circle with a diameter of some twenty-four kilometres.

There is no organization in Great Britain for what the Americans call 'the birders'. In the United States the whole sport of 'birding' or listing birds is much more highly developed than in Britain and the American Birders' Association is well organized with its own magazine *Birding*, which carries short articles on the best birdwatching places with precise direction to each bird, and long lists of birders with the longest life lists or the longest lists of birds seen in their own States. There is obviously competition – I am not certain that this helps accuracy and the certainty of identification.

Although there is no organization in the sense of an established club there are a number of bush-telegraph services in Britain which operate on a personal basis and which seem to be enormously effective in bringing people together from all parts of the British Isles as soon as any rare bird is discovered. The record for the largest number of birds seen in the British Isles is apparently held at present by Ron Johns who passed the four-hundred mark in 1977.

Overseas birdwatching Nowadays there are a number of opportunities to take package tours to many exciting and remote areas. You may try a tour organized by one of the travel operators who concentrate on 'special interest' tours, particularly those concerned with wildlife. You are usually accompanied by an expert who will help you get over all sorts of identification problems. They are often good value for money. Alternatively, you can take an ordinary package tour to some exotic place which provides the flight and hotel, and while you are there you can hire a car or use the local bus service to go out and search for birds.

You may well prefer to strike out on your own completely and here John Gooders' book *Where to Watch Birds in Britain and Europe* becomes useful. However, in covering the whole of Europe, Gooders has not been able to describe the interesting areas in such detail as his book on British sites, *Where to Watch Birds*. Another useful book is *A Guide to Birdwatching in Europe* edited by J. Ferguson-Lees, Q. Hockliffe and K. Zweeres. Both, in their different ways, help you to start your search and from that point you can study such maps as you can obtain for the area concerned, picking out likely spots, for example, bays along peaceful coastlines, mountains, lakes, bogs and forests. Stanfords of Long Acre, London, as well as being the main agents for the Ordnance Survey, carry an enormous range of foreign maps. If you have access to a good ornithological library you might find some books or articles on the area you intend to visit.

If you happen to know someone who has visited the area or lives there, then this is an obvious source of information. Secretaries of local birdwatching societies and conservation bodies overseas usually only have voluntary staff and it is really unfair to expect them to have time to act as travel agents. The RSPB does have local representatives in a number of countries who have volunteered to give information to other members.

A final word on human behaviour. It surprises me how often a Briton abroad thinks that he is freed from all standards of good behaviour and that he can do what he likes and disregards the fact that in other countries, as in Britain, land is privately owned. Sometimes, too, he forgets the first part of the birdwatchers' code, that the welfare of the bird must be his first concern.

Counting the birds

Whilst I enjoy the sheer variety of birds and particularly those new or exciting ones that I find for myself, I enjoy even more being a 'curious naturalist' and asking questions and finding answers about the activities of birds.

In order to study many of the different aspects of the lives of birds we have to count them. Counting can tell us how many birds make use of the whole or part of a habitat for such activities as feeding, nesting or roosting. Regular counts can show us if there are changes in numbers and, if this is the case, it may become important to discover the reasons. They could be seasonal, with some individuals migrating over long distances, some only a few kilometres, and other species from harsher climates coming to take their place. Counting by birdwatchers has in recent years shown that often changes have resulted from habitat destruction and environmental hazards, such as organo-chlorine pesticides, oil pollution and even, though it was thousands of kilometres away, the effect which a disastrous drought in the Sahel Region had on the European bird populations which wintered there. The 1976 summer drought in Britain affected our own garden birds according to Mr and Mrs P. Willson who were undertaking a garden bird survey for the BTO.

Recently the Natural Environmental Research Council reviewed current and past work concerned with the monitoring of populations and communities of living organisms in marine, terrestial and freshwater habitats, and one aspect which was very clear, was that the part played by amateur naturalists in many disciplines was most valuable. This NERC report entitled *Biological Surveillance*, defines the work as attempting to detect temporal and spatial changes and providing a capability for predicting future changes.

Counting birds is by no means easy. In some places, for instance, a small lake, you can see all the birds quite clearly but in a wood of the same size this is quite impossible. Birds and their habitats are so variable that different methods of counting are required for each of them. To make things more difficult there is no agreement as to the ideal method of counting. It is also difficult to be certain that one person's figures are comparable to another's, even when working in the same area.

Counts are either direct or based on some form of estimation. In a direct count you must be able to see each individual bird. This method is suitable for lakes, estuaries, seabird cliffs, open fields and small flocks of birds in

Estimating the numbers of birds in large flocks requires practice. Can you estimate the size of this flock of Knots and Turnstones in five seconds?

flight or at sea. If you cannot see all the birds at once, for instance, in a woodland habitat or when counting a very large and fast-flying flock, you should count one or more samples and calculate the total from those figures. **Direct counts** A direct count should produce a more exact figure as, with a small lake, you can see all the birds at once. If the lake is large, however, you can run into problems as a substantial portion of a flock might move to a part of the lake, as yet, uncounted. Recently, I have been counting birds, using the direct method, on Pakistan lakes. One of these lakes had a surface area of just over 18 square kilometres and, with a telescope from high ground, it was possible to count all the ducks, herons and other long-legged water birds from two positions. However, in order to identify and count the small waders, I had to visit many more places where previous experience had taught me that the birds tended to feed or nest. Another of the lakes had a surface area of 185 square kilometres. Here I had to drive some 120 kilometres around the lake, stopping on headlands and other vantage points from which I could scan large areas of water with a telescope. In addition to the problem that some of the birds might have moved substantial distances (which I don't think they often did), there was the problem that at 3 kilometres, particularly with some refraction in the air over the water, the identification of individual birds was not easy. Even when they were closer than this, the flocks were often so dense that it was impossible to enumerate them and I had to rely on estimates. Before all these counts I had made a preliminary reconnaissance of the lakes, mapping, as far as possible, the

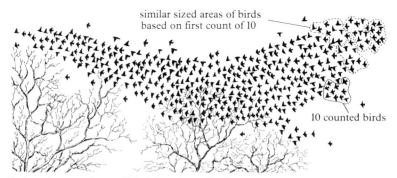

similar sized areas of birds based on first count of 10

10 counted birds

Estimating numbers of birds in a large flock

Some large flocks move too fast to be counted accurately. Count a group of ten or a hundred and estimate the number of tens or hundreds there are in the flock.

vegetation and learning the preferred feeding, loafing and sleeping areas of various species.

Closer to home, regular counts of lakes can be very useful. The results may be of value to the wildfowl counts which are organized in this country by the Wildfowl Trust, as well as by local county bird clubs. It is also worth counting any small area which can be seen easily, such as a pasture, field or estuary, especially if you visit it regularly. Over the years the results could show interesting changes.

Estimated counts The second method of arriving at a total number when counting birds is by estimating. This is done when direct counting is difficult or impossible due to the numbers of birds or the habitat. The operation almost invariably falls into two parts: firstly, a direct count of one or more samples is made and, secondly, a division of the flock is carried out using the size of the sample as the basic unit. For example, first count part of the flock, say ten birds, and then estimate how many groups of ten there are in the flock. The flock might be so large that the estimate will be in thousands. In order to account for any error an estimate of the largest and smallest size that the flock might be, should be given. Plenty of practice is needed and a useful aid to precision can be obtained if you photograph the flock and count the birds at leisure later and then compare this figure with your original estimate. Another problem for the unwary is that some birdwatchers tend to over-estimate the numbers of large birds and under-estimate the number of small birds. Whenever possible, it is a good idea to compare your counts with other people's. Whenever I see a group of birds I count them, this is done almost automatically dating from the years when I was a warden. Some of the results I will send to the county bird recorder.

Exactly the same principle of estimating is used when you are counting the number of birds in any habitat. Several methods may be used. In the breeding season you can attempt to locate all the nests in a part of a habitat but this is very time consuming and more often it is better to locate the singing males on the supposition that they are holding territory and are probably nesting. To obtain an estimate for the whole of a habitat, which should have approximately the same ecological structure, you census one or more sample areas and arrive at an average for the different species within the area. Then a calculation of the total size of the population is made by multiplying the population of sample area by the number of times that the total area is divisible by this sample area. For instance, the sample area may cover 8 hectares and the total area may be 80 hectares. The total number of pairs of Blue Tits in the sample area may be 9, therefore there will be approximately $\frac{80}{8} \times 9 = 90$ pairs. This system is commonly used for estimating game populations in the USA and some other countries.

Sometimes it is impractical or extremely difficult to count or even sample the number of birds. Therefore, bearing in mind that it is always best to give some idea of numbers, an indication of the maximum and minimum ranges can be given using a symbol for the order of size.

For instance:

1	1–10
2	11–100
3	101–1000
4	1 001–10 000
5	10 001–100 000
6	100 001–1 000 000

Common Birds Census The Common Birds Census was started in 1961. It is organized by the BTO and is the most satisfactory system for measuring bird populations, at present. If you wish to undertake a Common Birds Census in your area, you should get the full details from the BTO at Tring. Basically you select a study area ranging in size from approximately 20–25 hectares with woodland habitat to 80 hectares in open country such as farmland. You need to make eight or more visits lasting several hours, before the end of the summer. To have any value you must be prepared to carry this on over several seasons; continuity of record is most important. If you are working through the BTO 1:2500 outline maps will be provided free of charge. One of these should be used to show the major plant communities which are one of the main factors influencing the availability of nesting-sites and food; a standard lists of habitats is given on page 139.

Drawing any form of vegetation map has problems particularly for the birdwatcher, as it is more often the structure of the individual plant and, perhaps its fruit which is of fundamental importance to the bird. Very often a sketch of the profile of the habitat with some idea of the scale such as that on page 69 will give you a reasonable idea of the habitat. You can draw the basis of a vegetation map on the 1:10000 or the 1:25000 scale maps and then on these try to map the boundaries of the major plant communities such as grassland, heath, bracken, woodland, water and so on. You can indicate the distribution by symbols such as the initial two letters of the name. An example showing the vegetation map of Skokholm is shown on page 130. When you superimpose a map of the breeding distribution of various resident species you may be able to get some idea of the broad habitat requirement for the species. But in making your vegetation map the BTO recommend that in woodland areas you indicate whether the canopy is open or closed, and similarly describe the density of the field layers, e.g. dense, medium, sparse, giving the average heights and dominant species.

When actually recording in the field for the BTO Common Birds Census a separate trace of the base map is used for each visit to the study area. On this you plot the birds recorded. The following conventions are used by the BTO and are based on a system devised by a Norwegian ornithologist, A. Enemar. They are used here as though referring to a Blackbird (B):

Ⓑ	singing male
B	alarm call
B material	seen with nesting material in beak
B food	seen with food in beak
⁞BB⁞	two males fighting (movement of either breaking-up can be shown by arrow)
B★	nest
B or B♂ or B♀ or B juv.	sight record, with indication of sex and age, if appropriate
Ⓑ---Ⓑ	different birds in song at the same time
B♂ --- B♂	different birds in view at the same time
Ⓑ—Ⓑ	singing bird seen to take up new position
Ⓑ— ? —Ⓑ	thought to be the same bird, but not certain
B★--B★	nests in use at the same time and therefore different pairs.

When you have completed the fieldwork you can start analyzing the results. You take a fresh map for each species and transfer the symbols to the map, substituting the letter of the visit for the original symbol, accompanied by the appropriate convention. Therefore on the Blackbird map the symbol A now means Blackbird in song on the first visit; the second visit will have B and so on. When each map is complete it will show discrete groupings of letters indicating positions held by territorial males on different visits. Territory boundaries will be checked by BTO staff.

Line transect method While the Common Birds Census is the most precise method of censuring bird populations it is also somewhat time consuming and complicated. There are two further methods of sampling, which are simpler to use, although they forfeit some precision. The first of these methods is the line transect which is and has been used by people sampling a wide range of habitats in a number of different countries. This also has the advantage over the Common Birds Census in that it can be used throughout the year, enabling you to census winter populations.

On a line transect you walk through your chosen habitat along a regular path and record all the birds you identify either by sight or sound. You do not need to map their positions, although it is better if you do. There are, however, various conventions which you should observe. Most observers seem to recommend an average speed of about 3 kilometres an hour. Also you count all birds within 25 metres of the line. Some birds are more conspicuous than others and so it is difficult to compare results between one species and another or for one species from one wood to another, except where the birds are conspicuous. Nevertheless, the system can be quite useful for comparing a number of singing passerines.

I have used a line transect with some variations in a Cambridgeshire wood for three years. The wood from a historical and botanical viewpoint has Oak standards with Ash, Maple and Hazel coppicing. However, because the wood has not been coppiced for about seventy years, the Ash, in particular, has grown uncut with the result that over much of the wood it is already dominant and will take over when the present Oaks die.

I was interested in finding out the relative abundance of the various species of birds, both in the breeding season and during the winter, and also comparing the population with other woods. I counted the birds at monthly intervals. The transect was about 2 kilometres long and took an average of 118 minutes to complete. The table (page 67) shows only the commoner species in the wood and compares their figures with those obtained by Eric Simms in eighty-eight Oak woods and W. B. Yapp in thirteen Oak woods. The term relative abundance is used in all cases to express the total number of contacts with a species as a percentage of all contacts. The table shows that the most commonly recorded species in Hayley Wood was the Woodpigeon with a relative abundance of 16. If we compare the figures with those of Simms and Yapp and their sightings in Oak woods we find a surprising difference. They both clearly rate the Chaffinch as the most abundant species, with a relative abundance of 13 and 12 respectively compared to my rating of the Chaffinch as ninth with a relative abundance of only 3·2. There was also considerable difference in their sightings of the Willow Warbler.

I also compared my Hayley Wood results with lists of birds recorded by Simms and Yapp for Ash woods and found here that the commonest species was the Willow Warbler, closely followed by the Chaffinch and Woodpigeon. The point that interested me was the very low rating of the Chaffinch in Hayley Wood, as well as the Great Tit, Chiffchaff, Willow and Garden Warblers. Casual inspection of the woodland showed that it was similar to other Oak or Ash woods that I have visited. But the shrub layer did exhibit one feature which would explain some of the low ratings. This feature was the well marked 'browse' line just over a metre above the ground level which was the height to which a herd of Fallow Deer foraged. With the exception of the Chaffinch, for which no easy solution is evident, it is possible that the heavy grazing had removed the low cover in which the

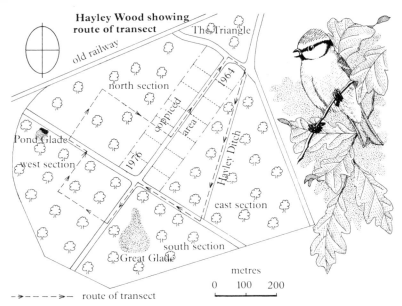

Hayley Wood showing route of transect

old railway

The Triangle

north section

1964

coppiced area

1976

Pond Glade

west section

Hayley Ditch

east section

south section

Great Glade

metres

0   100   200

→-----→- route of transect

During my survey of Hayley Wood in Cambridgeshire, I recorded all the birds seen or heard within twenty-five metres of a line transect which passed through the different woodland habitats.

warblers and, to some extent the Great Tit, nested and hunted for food.

From the figures resulting from the line transect, which is in effect a sample census, you can derive a rough estimate of the total number of birds in the wood. Furthermore, if you continue to make line transects throughout the year you can detect seasonal and annual variations in the bird populations.

When I am travelling and I have to move faster than a line transect allows, whether on foot or some form of transport such as a boat, I keep a fifteen minute check-list of the birds observed. Normally I use squared paper in my notebook, listing the birds on the left-hand side and using a column for each fifteen minutes. I use a 'tick' to record a sighting, or a figure, if I have counted, with an additional symbol for a song, nesting, etc. This can give some indication of the distribution of birds over a large area. If you can also add notes about the types of habitats through which you are passing, the record will be that much more valuable. Page 69 shows a sheet from my notebook and records the birds seen in fifteen minute periods through a forest edge with some open fields and finally through two kinds of forest, one grazed and the other ungrazed. Note the appearance of several warblers as soon as the forest edge appears. Two field-sketches show some of the salient features of the habitat.

HAYLEY WOOD

April, May and June 1973 to 1975   11 visits

	Total contacts	Average contacts	Relative abundance	Simms 88 woods rel. ab.	Yapp 13 woods rel. ab.
Woodpigeon	455	41·4 (1)	16·1 (1)	6 (6)	—
Jackdaw	206	18·7 (6)	7·3 (6)	—	—
Great Tit	68	6·2 (13)	2·4 (12)	4 (8)	3 (7)
Blue Tit	206	18·7 (6)	7·3 (6)	5 (7)	4 (6)
Long-tailed Tit	25	2·3 (19)	0·9 (20)	—	—
Wren	306	27·8 (2)	10·9 (2)	10 (4)	7 (4)
Song Thrush	214	19·4 (5)	7·6 (5)	3 (10)	2 (9)
Blackbird	254	23·1 (3)	9·0 (3)	8 (4)	7 (5)
Robin	222	20·9 (4)	7·8 (4)	11 (2)	7 (3)
Blackcap	79	7·2 (11)	2·3 (15)	2 (12)	—
Garden Warbler	32	2·9 (17)	1·1 (18)	3 (9)	1 (14)
Willow Warbler	145	13·2 (8)	5·1 (8)	7 (5)	9 (2)
Chiffchaff	36	3·3 (15)	1·3 (16)	—	2 (10)
Dunnock	67	6·1 (14)	2·4 (12)	2 (11)	—
Starling	89	8·1 (10)	3·1 (10)	—	—
Greenfinch	34	3·1 (16)	1·3 (17)	—	—
Bullfinch	28	2·5 (18)	1·0 (19)	—	—
Chaffinch	90	8·2 (9)	3·2 (9)	13 (1)	12 (1)
House Sparrow	68	6·2 (13)	2·4 (12)	—	—
Tree Sparrow	74	6·7 (12)	2·6 (11)	—	—

Length of line transect 2·1 km. Average time 118 minutes

22 other species recorded on the transects with a relative abundance of less than one

Spot census This is another sampling method which lacks many of the good qualities of the Common Birds Census, but it can be used throughout the year and is good for assessing the relative abundance of birds in different habitats. Spot censuses can be made in a number of ways. In Hayley Wood I used ten points which were roughly the same distance from each other and which were easily identified. I waited for five minutes recording all the birds which could be seen or heard within a 25 metre radius.

Counting cliff-nesting birds As fears grew about the pollution of the sea and its effect on seabird populations ornithologists attempted in 1969, to count the number of seabirds that breed around the coast of Britain, in an exercise known as 'Operation Seafarer'. This was organized by the Seabird Group and the results were published in a book called *The Seabirds of Britain and Ireland*, by Stanley Cramp, W. R. P. Bourne and David Saunders. The book also discusses seabird populations and the methods of

Hayley Wood	April 28th 1978		E2. Sun thro' thin cloud.	
Wren	ssssssssssssss	(15)	Great Tit sss2.s	7
Greenfinch	.	1	Chiff-chaff ssss	4
Chaffinch	.s	2	Willow Warbler ssssss	6
Blue Tit	.2..2.s....s	15	Redpoll .	1
Blackbird	s.......s...s2..	17	Jackdaw ...	3
Song Thrush	sssssssss	9	Marsh Tit s	.
Starling	2..	4	Cuckoo s	.
Woodpigeon	s..2.....20.	31	Red-Leg'd Part. 2.	2
Bullfinch	.	1	Pheasant .	.
Gt. Spt. Woodpecker	N.B.	.	Yellowhammer .	.
Robin	.ss	3	Lr. Spt. Woodpecker 2.	2
Blackcap	s	.	Jay .	.
Stock Dove	ss	2	Green Woodpecker Y	.
Tree Sparrow	2.2	4		
Dunnock	s.s	2		

Hayley Wood – page from notebook

This is a page from my field notebook showing the results of a two kilometre line transect through Hayley Wood in April.

censusing different species. At present the RSPB co-ordinates sample counts of some colonies of cliff-nesting birds. Those interested in seabirds should also consult the bulletins and reports of the Seabird Group, which contain papers on methods of counting seabirds and give the results of such counts in various parts of the British Isles.

The counting of seabirds on nesting cliffs in large colonies can be very difficult and, for the fool-hardy, dangerous. It might be quite simple to count the number of individual birds on some cliffs, but that figure does not tell you the numbers that are really nesting there, for you cannot always see the eggs or young birds. Clare Lloyd, who has counted Razorbills and Guillemots for some years, has pointed out some of the hazards which could lead to errors in the results. For example, there can be considerable variations in the number of auks visiting the colonies at different times of the day. The numbers are least variable just before the young hatch, particularly in June and she recommends that five to ten counts should be undertaken at this time, as near mid-day as possible, when the error is reduced to between 5% and 17% for Razorbills and 4% to 8% for Guillemots.

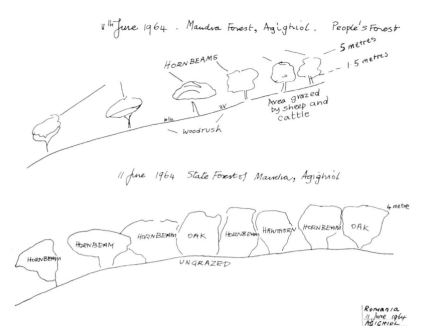

11th June 1964. Maudra Forest, Agighiol. People's Forest

HORNBEAMS — 5 metres — 1.5 metres

Area grazed by sheep and cattle

— Woodrush

11 June 1964 State Forest of Maudra, Agighiol

4 metre

HORNBEAM — HORNBEAM — HORNBEAM — OAK — HORNBEAM — HAWTHORN — HORNBEAM — OAK

UNGRAZED

When walking long distances or travelling by train with little time to count birds, a record of birds seen every ten or fifteen minutes will give a better idea of their abundance and distribution than a single list. Some rough field sketches of the habitat types you have passed through will also add valuable information to the list.

Romania
11 June 1964
Agighiol

Close to start with, then thundery.

	10.45	11.00	11.15	11.30	11.45	12.00	12.15	12.30	12.45	13.00/13.15 13.30	11
Ortolan	s	✓	s	s	c	.	s	s	s	s	10
Bee eater	✓					.			o		2
Hoodie	o	✓		✓	✓	✓.	✓	✓	✓		9
Magpie	2	✓	✓	✓	✓	✓.	✓	✓	✓		7
Imp. Eagle	1					.					1
Oriole	s	s	s	s	✓	s.	s	s	s	s	11
Tree Sparrow	c					c.					2
Blue Tit	c				c	.		✓			3
Kestrel	✓			✓		.					2
Swallow		o		o	o	o . o	o	o	o		8
Chaffinch	s	s	s	s	s	c					6
Great Tit		✓	✓		c	. c					4
Turtle Dove	s	s		✓	.	s	s	s	s		7
Starling			o			.	o				2
Tree Pipit		s				.					1
Skylark				s		.					1
Swift				o		.					1
Sand Martin					o.		✓	✓			3
Hoopoe						✓ o					2
Sprosser					.s	s	s	s	s		5
Wood Warbler					.s						1
Blackcap					.s	s					2
House Martin						.	o	o	o		3
Whitethroat					.			s	s		2

(column notes at bottom, written vertically:) Wood edge. Himus etc. / 15ft high. Oak, hornbeam. Sheep / Hornbeam / Spring corn & Hornbeam / Trees & valley & wheat / Shallow lakes, grass / Shal. pools / State For. / Ostriva / no undergrowth.

It is not always possible to see from one point the whole of a very extensive tern or gull colony on flat ground. In these colonies it is possible to count a sample area and estimate the total from this. However, these colonies should not be disturbed unless it is for an important scientific reason and then only by an ornithologist who knows what he is doing.

Counting birds on cliffs poses yet more problems. Unless it is a very small colony you will probably not be able to see all the birds at once. You, therefore, have to move your position to get a new angle on the colony and have the added difficulty of determining whether you are looking at the edge of the section you have just counted, or, indeed, whether you have missed some. Counting from a boat is not easy since, more often than not, it moves up and down! Photography of a cliff from a boat or land and then a later count can help too, but, if you have a mixed colony, identification is virtually impossible.

When counting such colonies cameras that produce an instant print might well be invaluable in providing a basis for a sketch on which you can mark the ledges you have been counting. Using your print or sketch you would be able to number the ledges and mark in the count for each ledge.

Beached Bird Survey The Beached Bird Survey is organized by the RSPB in conjunction with the Seabird Group. The original idea of this scheme which was started many years ago, was to monitor the effect of oil pollution on seabirds. It is still used for that purpose but also recently gave the first indication of the mass deaths of birds resulting, in part, from the dumping of polychlorinated biphenyls (PCB's) in the Irish Sea and, also in part, from storm stress. The procedure is for one observer to walk regularly along one stretch of shore and count corpses. Normally, counts are required for five specified weekends in each winter but regular visits at dates other than those of the national or international counts have often given the first warnings that some catastrophe has affected birds out at sea. The system when carried on for some years probably provides a useful working baseline for showing up incidents of mortality within, what one of the observers calls, 'the corpse catchment area'.

My purpose in this chapter has been to take you beyond identification and to show how counting birds provides a means to answering questions about birds. However, when you get to the stage when you want to get really scientific you will need to read the relevant scientific papers before you start. Almost every year either the BTO, RSPB or the Wildfowl Trust organize projects of one sort or another in which help from the amateur birdwatcher is required.

The lives of birds

In the previous chapters I have been writing about the way to watch and count birds and the equipment such as binoculars, field guides and field notebook that you will need. Now it is time to look at the ways birds live so that you can begin to understand what they are doing. In a book of this size it is only possible to give a summary of their nesting behaviour, how they are distributed, how and where they feed. You will find further information in the books and journals listed in the appendices. But I hope that the summary I give in the next few chapters will introduce you to different aspects of a bird's life and help you to understand what you see when you watch a bird.

Seeking answers about migration, breeding behaviour or biology needs patience and accuracy as well as a deep and lasting curiosity. You will develop a deeper understanding of the way birds live and behave, and the ways by which they are linked to their environment. The ecology of birds fascinates many ornithologists with different levels of scientific experience; indeed, some aspects are highly complicated and require not only the skills of a naturalist but also considerable skill as a mathematician. However, it has been well proven that there is much valuable work that we, as ordinary naturalists, can do in this field.

A few years ago when fewer people were interested in natural history and less was known about birds, it was possible for any ornithologist who wanted to concentrate on some specific study to contribute something new to our knowledge of birds. Nowadays, however, a lot more is known about the lives of birds and one has to work a great deal harder to discover something new to science. In whichever way we watch birds for many of us their study in itself gives us a great deal of pleasure and the fact that we might not produce anything new to science is less important than the fact that we are learning something for ourselves.

In order to apply some of the mechanics of birdwatching that have been described it is useful to know something of the biological and behavioural aspects of a bird's life.

The origin of birds T. H. Huxley, the great evolutionist, called birds 'glorified reptiles' for quite clearly they have evolved from reptiles. Their early ancestors were similar to some of the dinosaurs of the Triassic period, millions of years ago. These were long-tailed, long-legged, lizard-like creatures, which ran about usually on their hind legs, flapping their wings and occasionally flying short distances. The *Archaeopteryx*, which is considered to be the oldest known bird, lived about 140 million years ago in the late Jurassic period; its fossils were found in 1861 and again in 1898 in Bavaria. It was about the size of a Magpie with a reptilean-type brain; it had jaws that had sockets to hold teeth, and a long bony tail. Although it is considered to be a bird, it had not adapted to flight in the same way as modern birds. Each of its 'hands' had three fingers and there was no sign of any fusion of the 'hand' and 'wristbone' as there is in modern species. Also its bones do not appear to have been honey-combed with air-spaces as they are in modern birds.

Present day birds and reptiles still have common characteristics. Certain skeletal and muscular features are common to both; they both lay eggs and both have a horny protuberance on their bill or snout, known as the egg-tooth, which appears for a short time when the bird or reptile hatches. Both birds and reptiles lay eggs but birds' eggs differ from those of reptiles in that many of them are coloured. Differences include the facts that birds usually guard their eggs whereas reptiles tend not to; young birds usually need care and feeding but the young of reptiles are independent at once; birds and mammals are warm-blooded but the body temperature of reptiles generally fluctuates with changes in air temperature, and therefore, they are more active on warm days. The feature which really sets birds apart from reptiles is that they are covered with feathers instead of scales, and that, with a few exceptions, they can fly.

Evolution is not something that only happened in the past; it is continuous throughout time. At present there are about 8,600 species of birds in the world and the process of natural selection is continuing with new species arising and others failing to compete. Natural selection is a process by which only those animals and plants best adapted to their environment survive. The young of all animals and plants, while conforming to the general pattern and shape of the species, also have their own individual characteristics. In a brood some will be bigger and stronger than others; various parts of their bodies may differ in size, some may have sharper sight or hearing than others allowing them to find food more easily or to avoid their enemies more quickly. Some may be able to react instinctively or more rapidly than others or to learn more quickly. Before long the young have to leave the care of their parents and find their own food, they may even have to fly long distances on migration, avoiding predatory birds on the way and a new set of hazards on their arrival in their winter quarters.

Some birds may not be so efficient at nesting, for instance, a pair of Goldfinches I once watched in Germany, failed, I was convinced, because of the male's lack of attentiveness to the female. His failure to feed her when she was on the nest resulted in her having to leave to feed herself so often that the eggs never hatched. All these natural factors and many others weed out the less able to ensure that generally the best adapted for the conditions of life, survive to reproduce.

Populations of a species which has a wide distribution will perhaps be affected by different environmental factors in various parts of its range which may result over the years in the evolution of a slightly different version of the same species. This difference may take the form of a change in size or colouring or even different habits. If sufficient numbers of a population exhibit these divergent characteristics they may be considered by taxonomists to merit a special subspecific name. Finally, if this group is independent for long enough, it may develop sufficiently different characteristics from its parent stock and if, by chance, the two groups should meet again they would no longer be able to interbreed and will thus have become a distinct species.

Now it so happens that over the years certain species have been unable to adapt to changes in the environment. Some of these changes have been hastened by man who has for agricultural reasons, perhaps, stripped vast stretches of forest of trees or drained marshes with the result that some populations of rare birds have been put in danger of extinction. Some, indeed, have become extinct because of man's actions. However, while man's activities have been harmful, we can now interfere with events and if some bird is in danger of extinction we can afford it some measure of protection. An example of this is the recent recovery of the population of the Hawaiian Goose, or Ne Ne. In 1949 only about thirty or forty of these geese were still known to exist having declined from a one-time estimated population of 5,000. Thanks to Sir Peter Scott, the Hawaiian authorities, New Zealand and the USA, the population has been able to steadily increase recently.

Anatomy The structure of most birds is related to their ability to fly and this imposes a number of restrictions on their bone structure and body shape. Because a bird can fly it is desirable that its bones should not only be strong but also light. To achieve this some bones have air spaces or cavities which are crossed by bony struts to strengthen them. Pneumatization, as this is called, occurs chiefly in the wing and other large bones, and even the skull has some of these small air recesses. These cavities are particularly well developed in large gliding and soaring birds such as vultures, albatrosses and eagles but are less so in diving birds such as ducks and cormorants, presumably because any additional bouyancy would require extra energy on the part of the bird when it wanted to dive. Some of the bones have also been strengthened during the course of evolution by the fusion of many of the bones of their reptilian ancestors. On the other hand, the flexibility of the neck has been increased by the large number of vertebrae, ranging from thirteen in the Cuckoo and other song birds to as many as twenty-eight in the swan. This gives the bird freedom to move its head while searching for food, watching for enemies, preening and so on.

The most obvious features of a bird's skeleton are the skull, the backbone or vertebral column, the pectoral girdle which houses the wing bones, the bones of the pelvic girdle to which are attached the legs, and the ribs which protect the body cavity. The other prominent feature is the breast bone or sternum which has a noticeable keel to which the wing muscles are

Skeleton of a pigeon

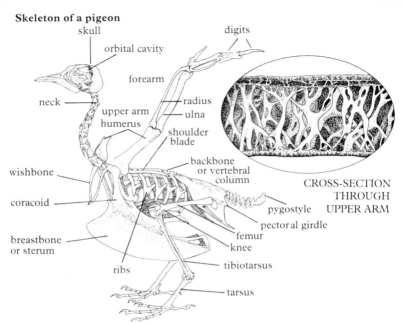

skull

orbital cavity

digits

forearm

neck

radius

ulna

upper arm
humerus

shoulder
blade

backbone
or vertebral
column

wishbone

coracoid

pygostyle

CROSS-SECTION
THROUGH
UPPER ARM

pectoral girdle

breastbone
or sterum

femur
knee

ribs

tibiotarsus

tarsus

The skeleton of a bird must provide a strong but light framework. Hollow bones with cross-struts help reduce weight yet give adequate strength.

attached. Generally speaking, the stronger the flyer the deeper the keel; in some flightless birds the keel has entirely disappeared.

I will not describe the entire structure of the bird, which is shown above, but it is worth mentioning some external features. The upper and lower mandibles (the bill) are a bony adaptation of the skull which are covered with a horny sheath. The shape of the bill is usually adapted to a bird's feeding behaviour, but occasionally as with Puffins and herons the formation of the bill plays an important part in the bird's displays. Flesh-eating species such as hawks, owls, shrikes and even the fish-eating shearwaters have hooked bills for tearing their prey. Some waders such as Snipe have long thin bills which they use for probing deeply into the mud; the tip is sensitive so that they can detect their prey. Nightjars on the other hand have short, but very wide bills, which enable them to catch flying insects more easily. Even amongst the finches there is a variety of shapes and sizes, from the Goldfinch's long and thin bill, which is used for poking into Teazel florets, to the twisted bill of the Crossbill, which is used for extracting seed from conifer cones. Birds do not have real teeth although several species have appendages which have the appearance of teeth.

The nostrils are situated in the upper mandible and open into a nasal cavity. In the petrels and a number of related seabirds the nostrils are

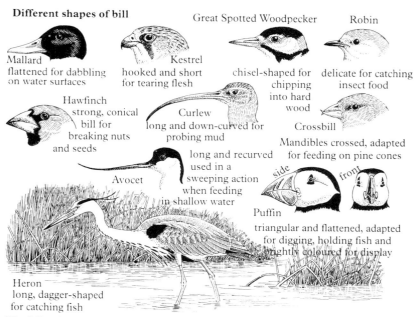

Different shapes of bill

Great Spotted Woodpecker

Robin

Mallard
flattened for dabbling
on water surfaces

Kestrel
hooked and short
for tearing flesh

chisel-shaped for
chipping
into hard
wood

delicate for catching
insect food

Hawfinch
strong, conical
bill for
breaking nuts
and seeds

Curlew
long and down-curved for
probing mud

Crossbill

Mandibles crossed, adapted
for feeding on pine cones

Avocet
long and recurved
used in a
sweeping action
when feeding
in shallow water

side

front

Puffin
triangular and flattened, adapted
for digging, holding fish and
brightly coloured for display

Heron
long, dagger-shaped
for catching fish

The bills of birds are adapted to their feeding and sometimes to their courtship requirements.

modified into a horny tube. In Gannets and Cormorants, the nostrils are completely closed and it is assumed that they breathe through their mouth.

Legs and toes vary enormously. The four toes are attached to the tarsus and they can be arranged in a variety of ways depending on the methods the bird uses to hunt its food. In most perching birds three toes point forward and one points to the rear. This arrangement suits best the way of life which involves perching on branches and twigs. There is enormous variation in the actual shape of the toes and I feel that the relationship of the feet to the habitat is still a fairly open field for discovery. Woodpeckers which cling to the sides of trees have two claws pointing forwards and two backwards, one of which they can move forward to make three. Walking and running birds like the Lapwing have short toes with longer legs, while other walking birds like the Meadow Pipit have long hind claws, presumably to allow them to walk over the longer grasses, without entangling their feet. Swimming birds need their legs to be located near the hind part of the body where they can best control the steering. The legs of some species are flattened laterally and are articulated so that they can be slipped forward through the water with as little resistance as possible.

Muscles The body of a bird has about 175 muscles most of which are paired. The largest and most powerful are the pectoral muscles which in a strong flyer can weigh as much as 30% of the bird's total weight. These are the muscles which pull the wings downwards and forwards. Muscles cannot push so another muscle which rests below the wing and which is connected to the humerous by a tendon comes into play, acting as a pulley to lift the wing. The legs also have powerful muscles which are used both for locomotion and maintaining the bird's position when perched. These large muscles in the legs and wings are near the body's centre of gravity and the main mass of muscle is located, therefore, high over the femur.

Locomotion Birds move about either by use of their wings or their legs. Some birds use one method of locomotion more than the other. The Ostrich has lost the power of flight and to compensate has very powerful legs. On the other hand, the legs of some seabirds like petrels are particularly well-adapted for swimming but hardly support the bird's weight on land. The Swift is another example of a bird which has specialized in flight, to the extent that its legs are so weak that it cannot stand upright and seldom lands on the ground.

It is a bird's power of flight which sets it apart from most other vertebrate animals. With this ability they are able to exploit the air into which they can escape from terrestial predators and through which they can move freely and hunt. A bird's wing has a curved surface, which is rounded above and hollow below, with a wedge-shaped profile. As the air flows past the wing it creates what is known as drag and lift. Drag, as the name suggests, results from the resistance of the air to the passage of the wing through it. Lift is caused by the air passing over the curved surface more quickly than under it, because the air under the wing has a slightly greater distance to travel. This difference causes a partial vacuum above the wing and pressure below which, together, creates lift.

The angle which the wing makes with the horizontal is called the angle of attack and at its optimum angle the amount of lift created by the air flowing past the wing counteracts the forces of gravity. As the angle of attack is

These drawings show how the powerful muscles which operate the wings are brought into play.

Diagram of the wing mechanism

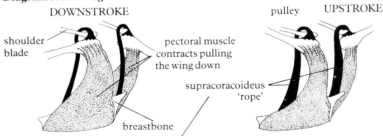

As the pectoral muscle releases the supracoracoideus contracts acting as a 'rope' with the end of the shoulder blade acting as the pulley to raise the wing

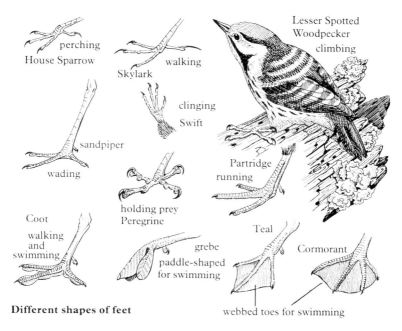

Different shapes of feet

Lesser Spotted Woodpecker climbing

House Sparrow perching

Skylark walking

Swift clinging

sandpiper wading

Partridge running

holding prey Peregrine

Coot walking and swimming

grebe paddle-shaped for swimming

Teal

Cormorant

webbed toes for swimming

These drawings indicate what a wide variety of legs and claws birds have evolved in response to their various means of locomotion.

increased the smooth flow of air over the wing breaks down and becomes turbulent which slows the bird down, until, when the bird is about to stall, the alula or bastard wing and other slotting devices come into play. The air then rushes through these slots keeping the flow over the wing fast and free of turbulence. Incidentally, this type of slot can be seen on the forewing of aircraft.

Flapping flight is highly complicated and, in fact, is not fully understood yet. Generally speaking, forward propulsion is provided mainly by the wing tips or the primaries and the chief function of the secondary feathers is to give lift – they move relatively little as the wing beats. On the down beat the wings move powerfully not only downwards but forwards with the feathers closed. The flight feathers are flexible and twist like a propeller so that the downward movement pulls the bird through the air. On the upstroke, which also drives the bird through the air although fractionally less powerfully, the primaries open like a venetian blind to allow the air through. The bird rotates its wings at the shoulder to increase the angle of attack in order to maintain lift and once again the primaries are bent on the upstroke. If a bird wishes to alter course it can do so by tilting its body or adjusting its wings and tail.

Taking-off can be difficult for birds. Swans have to run to attain the necessary air speed, auks need a vertical cliff to jump off, while others like some of the vultures have difficulty raising themselves from the ground unless it is sufficiently heated to provide strong thermals. Passerines on the other hand can take-off simply by jumping into the air. They obtain the forward thrust they need by flicking their wings backwards during the upstroke and obtain the required lift by using a powerful downstroke.

Once in the air a bird can glide without beating its wings for various lengths of time depending upon the shape of the wings and the body length. Some birds, like the gulls and albatrosses, are able to glide rapidly, while slower gliding birds such as the broad-winged hawks and vultures tend to lose height more slowly. Many birds are able to soar making use of up-currents. Fulmars and gulls make use of these along cliffs; petrels and shearwaters glide along ocean waves; buzzards use the rising currents over hills and vultures and many other species use the warm thermals. Some birds can hover by reducing their speed to that of the wind but real hovering birds such as Kestrels and terns have to take a nearly vertical stance and beat their wings backwards and forwards in a horizontal plane.

Digestive system The digestive system is based on a tube which runs through the bird from its mouth to cloaca. Along this tube various glands secrete the chemicals which break down the food into substances which the body cells can assimilate. Some birds have saliva glands which lubricate the food but others, including most waterbirds, are entirely without them; for instance, on the Island of Skokholm the Great Black-backed Gulls took their food to the sea to eat. From the base of the neck the oesophagus or gullet which is a thin-walled tube opens out into a balloon-like crop. This crop varies in size from almost nothing in some meat-eaters to a huge sack-like store in grain-eaters like the Woodpigeon. Here the food is stored and moistened before passing on to the stomach. The pigeon's crop is particularly interesting in the breeding season, as it secretes a substance known as pigeon's milk which is sloughed off the side of the gullet and regurgitated for the young.

Leaving the crop, the food moves down into the stomach where it is first treated with enzymes and then subjected to the grinding action of the muscles of the gizzard combined with the abrasive effect of small stones which collect there and which some species pick-up deliberately.

The metabolism of birds is so high that energy is used quickly. Carnivorous birds digest large quantities of food very rapidly. Seedeaters take longer to assimilate the greater quantities of less nourishing food, indeed, small birds seem to be constantly swallowing at one end and ejecting at the other.

Reproductive system In male birds the two testes lie within the body cavity fairly close to the kidneys. From each of these there is a minute duct leading to the cloaca. Adult female birds, unlike other vertebrates, have only one functional ovary and oviduct – the left-hand one – in which a number of ovum develop but only a few ripen during the breeding season.

Large birds of prey such as this Griffon Vulture rely on rising warm air currents to help save energy. Since little warm air rises over the sea migrating raptors make for the shortest sea-crossings.

When it ripens the ovum bursts its follicle and is caught up by the funnel-like entrance to the oviduct down which it moves. During copulation, the hindmost part of the cloaca is turned outwards, and held tightly to that of the male. The male reproductive cells are then ejected directly into the female cloaca and move up the oviduct to fertilize each descending ovum. Gradually albumen is deposited around the yolk and, finally the shell membrane and the shell itself are added to the egg in the uterus.

During the greater part of the year the sexual organs are very small but with the coming of the breeding season they enlarge considerably. In the House Sparrow the sexual organs may weigh hundreds of times more in the breeding season than during the rest of the year.

Feather structure Feathers, which distinguish birds from other animals, develop from a knob or papilla located within a feather socket or follicle. The material of which the feather is composed is basically the same as that in the horn on their bills and the scales on their feet. Feathers are of two main types; firstly, there are the flight and contour feathers which give the bird its shape and provide outer insulation. Secondly, there are the down feathers which are found beneath the contour feathers and provide extra-insulation All other feathers are intermediate between these two. Herons and other waterbirds, as well as some birds of prey have special powder-down feathers which grow continuously and gradually disintegrate into a fine powder which is used in feather maintenance and cleanliness. The standard feather has a shaft of which the lowest part, called the calamus, is embedded in the feather follicle. The shaft is hollow, has no veins and is translucent. The lower end tapers to a point through which, when the feather is growing, nutrients enter. The upper part of the shaft, called the rachis, supports the feather vanes. These vanes are more or less flexible and consist of hundreds of filaments called barbs. Every barb carries several hundred tiny barbules equipped with minute hooks, known as barbicels. These catch on the barbules from the next barb above them creating a most efficient fastening system, which is similar to the velcro system used on anoraks. If the weather tears open the barbs all the bird has to do is draw the feathers through its beak and the filaments knit together again.

Function of feathers Feathers have many different and important functions: they are used for conserving warmth, for flying, and for protecting the bird against knocks. The colour of the feathers is important for both camouflage and courtship displays. During the winter the contour feathers are fluffed out in order to trap a thick pocket of warm air between the feathers and the skin; conversely on hot days in summer they are ruffled to allow hot air to escape more easily. This adaption for conserving heat is necessary because a bird must maintain a body temperature of 41°C since the metabolism which produces the vast amount of energy required for flight, goes on much more rapidly the higher the body temperature. Although birds do not perspire they can control their body temperature within quite narrow limits.

The number of feathers varies considerably from one species to another; for instance, the density of feathering on waterfowl is greater than in other species, presumably to protect them from their coldwater environment. A count of feathers from a Whistling Swan revealed a total of no less than 25,216 individual feathers, including the down feathers. Feathers do not grow in a random fashion from all over a bird's body but in most species they are confined to definite tracts.

Feather colour Two of the functions of feather colour appear to be contradictory: one is self-advertisement and the other is self-concealment. In many species a balance is struck between these needs, the male being brightly coloured, especially in the breeding season, and the female being camouflaged by drab coloration. In the Dotterel and the Red-necked Phalarope the normal coloration and roles are reversed and the male, which is more drabbly coloured, incubates the eggs and looks after the young. In many species their striking colours can be used for both functions depending on the posture the bird adopts. For instance, the black patches of the Wheatear can be used as self-advertisement when the bird is displaying but also helps to disguise it when it is motionless amidst the rocks and stones. Furthermore, self-advertisement has the dual purpose of threatening or attracting females and thus we find that one colour in a bird can carry several messages.

The colours in the feathers are due either to the chemical substances deposited in the feathers or to their physical properties. Reds, yellows, blacks, browns and greens are usually due to the chemical properties but some greens are produced by structural conditions. Iridescent colours which are one form of structural colouring are produced from the barbules that may be flattened for part of their length or twisted and whose successive surfaces interfere with the lightwaves. Some colours, especially black, which is based on the pigment melanin, tend to be more resistant to wear. On beaches you can often find worn gull feathers in which the flecks of white have worn away whereas the black areas are still intact.

Feather moult To be at peak efficiency throughout a bird's life feathers have to be shed and renewed once or twice a year, depending on the species of bird. In almost all species a few feathers are renewed at a time, usually in pairs on either side of the body. The moulting of the wing feathers seriously impairs the ability of a bird to fly and in some cases prevents it from flying altogether. Drakes lose all their flight feathers at once and are therefore flightless for some weeks in late summer, this is when they are said to be in 'eclipse'. However, their marshy habitat at this season of the year usually provides them with adequate food and shelter, and their sober 'eclipse' plumage affords them extra camouflage.

Normally birds do not moult during the breeding season, on migration or during times of food shortage as they need all the energy they can obtain to generate new feathers and to replace heat loss during the moult. However, there are all sorts of odd exceptions. Seabirds moult during the breeding season which is probably because it is safer to moult while they are on land than when they are out at sea. Migratory birds usually moult after the breeding season when there is plenty of food available and before their long flight to their winter quarters. Other species migrate to relatively safe areas to moult, the Shelduck, for example, uses Bridgewater Bay in Somerset and the Eider Duck collects off the coast of Aberdeenshire in July. The Common Scoter gathers in flocks of 150,000 birds in one spot off the Danish coast.

Some birds moult more than once a year. The Ptarmigan moults three times: one complete autumn moult produces its brown plumage, two partial moults produce the white winter plumage and then a third moult gives it the grey spring plumage. The Purple Sandpiper has what is known as an 'arrested' moult which begins in the breeding grounds and then continues in the winter quarters, after migration. This arrested moult may result from the fact that large birds take a long time to moult and cannot afford to wait too long as the summer food supply soon becomes exhausted. This is a particular danger if the birds happen to be insectivorous.

The time taken for moulting and changing feathers varies enormously. Some long distance migrants can lose and replace their feathers within thirty-five days prior to the migration. Others such as the Redpoll can take as much as fifty days. The Curlew Sandpiper, and shore waders which moult when they reach their winter quarters can take six or seven months to moult; eagles can take more than a year with several arrests.

The bright new feathers of a bird's spring plumage are not always the result of a spring moult. Sometimes the brightly coloured feathers grow in the autumn but are tipped with a duller colour. In spring the tip is lost by abrasion and the brighter colours are revealed. One obvious example is provided by the black breast of the House Sparrow which is hidden by the grey feather tips in winter.

Feather maintenance Proper maintenance ensures that the feathers are kept in good condition between moults. Preening is the most important form of maintenance and a bird will spend quite a large proportion of its day pulling feathers through the tip of its bill to clean them and zip up any loose barbs. It will also peck at its feathers to remove foreign matter including feather parasites. The bird will work through the various feather tracts, lifting its wings to peck at the primaries and turning its head through all sorts of angles to get at the rump and tail feathers. It is impossible for a bird to preen its own head so it resorts to scratching it with one foot while balancing on the other. Some fish-eating birds, such as Herons, Cormorants and Gannets have a comb on the inside edge of a hind toe, this is known as a pectinated claw and is helpful in removing fish slime from feathers. The insect-eating Nightjar also has a pectinated claw.

Bathing When there is water available, bathing may often precede the daily routine of feather maintenance. Everyone who has a bird-bath or pond in their garden can watch Blackbirds and other birds regularly having a splash. The point of bathing is not to wash the feathers so much as to dampen them so that the oiling which follows next is more effective: the washing of feathers and skin seems to be of only secondary importance. A Blackbird, when it bathes, stands mostly in shallow water often with its feathers fluffed up. It dips its head under the water, in such a way that the water is scooped up and falls over its back, or else it will bend forward and put its bill in the water and with its feathers fluffed, splash water with its wings. A moment or two later it will sit back in the water with its tail low and by flicking the tail upwards will splash water over its body.

Other species have very different methods of bathing. Swallows and terns bathe in flight by dashing themselves into the water and sending up a shower of spray, then flying on with hardly a hesitation. Kingfishers dive repeatedly into the water and then preen themselves on a nearby perch, while ducks use the safety of the water where they can dive or swim away from any danger. Some species such as pigeons and Starlings will bathe in the rain with their wings spread out.

Birds only need to dampen their feathers; if they get them too wet this will affect their ability to fly and is therefore dangerous. Many birds have a 'rain-posture' during which they stand upright with their feathers close to the body so that the rain runs off the plumage quite rapidly.

The reason the Cormorant and to a lesser extent the Shag hang out their wings in this way is still not clear; whether it is to dry out the feathers is still disputed by ornithologists.

The most common method of removing the moisture from the feathers is to raise and then depress the contour feathers and at the same time relax and jerk the body forward. Waterbirds, which dry themselves while resting on the water, raise and flap their wings in addition to this movement. Cormorants and Shags leave the water to preen their feathers and can be regularly seen standing on rocks and posts with their wings outstretched; why they should do this is still not clear. Ducks and some gulls also perform special movements in flight to shake water off their feathers; gulls can often be seen shaking their wings and bodies in flight after bathing.

Oiling After bathing and drying a bird may smear oil on to the feathers from the oil gland which is situated just above the rump. The oil gland is largest in some of the seabirds and waterbirds and may be partly related to their aquatic life and help with waterproofing, but there is still debate as to the true function of this gland which is missing from Woodpeckers and some other species. The oil is an acid fatty secretion and in some species, such as the female and young of Hoopoes, smells offensively. It has also been suggested that it helps to preserve the horny covering of the bill. Furthermore there is some experimental evidence that the secretion applied to the plumage may enable vitamin D to be synthesized under the influence of sunlight and then presumably absorbed either through the skin or ingested in subsequent preening.

Sunning Several species of birds can be found deliberately exposing their bodies to the sun using a special posture. As with other feather-maintenance activities there is some controversy as to the cause and

83

Shallow birdbaths can easily be made from an old dustbin lid. Many birds like this thrush dip their heads into the water, swill it over their backs and then spash it with their wings.

function of this behaviour. Some people consider that the posture in which the bird lies on its belly with wings and tail spread widely, is a simple response to temperature. Sometimes, the wings may be raised and feathers twisted round – a position which may vary according to the species. However, this may not be the whole story because, while young birds react as though it were a simple temperature response, adults may react to a image of the sun. Even on cool days exposure to the sun changes the chemical quantity of oil from the preen gland, and maybe it is the light rather than the warmth which is biologically important. Blackbirds which sunbathe regularly also seem to have a regular place to do it. However I have not seen this recorded for other species.

Dusting Some species of bird, particularly game birds and others which may have originated from arid areas, dust themselves by driving sand and other fine particles amongst their feathers. They will find a dusty hollow and drive the dust into the feathers either by shuffling themselves or by scratching the dust with their feet, sometimes both the wings and feet are used. House Sparrows, as many keen gardeners know, frequently dust themselves. Why this is done is not fully understood but it may have something to do with dislodging or discouraging the feather and skin parasites.

Anting In addition to all these methods of feather maintenance some passerines anoint themselves with the body fluid of ants. The bird which I have seen doing this most often is the Starling. The important part of the

A Blackbird sunning. The exact purpose of this activity, which often occurs after preening, oiling or dusting, is still something of a mystery. In this posture the oil gland at the base of the tail is exposed.

fluid is formic acid which is produced by some worker ants but fluids from other groups of ants are also used. Once again nobody is certain as to the function of this behaviour. However, it probably assists in the care of the feathers as formic acid is known to be an insecticide and may kill or discourage the ectoparasites. Anting is actually carried out by the bird smearing ants with its bill directly on to the feathers or by letting the ants swarm over it and penetrate between the feathers while ejecting their formic acid.

The five senses *Vision* This is of prime importance as it allows them to find their food, to avoid their enemies and to recognize their mates. Some birds have a very highly developed sense of sight which is not surprising when one remembers how fast a bird has to react to so many different stimulae. Some birds have an eyesight which is eight times keener than man's. Birds have the ability to change focus rapidly and have a comparatively large eyeball. Relatively speaking a Starling's eyeball is fifteen times heavier than a man's; an eagle's eyeball is actually larger than a man's. They are generally so large that there is little room for movement and as a result birds have very flexible necks and most species can rotate their heads through 180°. Birds can also see through a much wider angle as a result of the position of the eye in the head. An owl can see through about 100°, up to 70° of which will be binocular vision while a pigeon can see through 340°, only a small percentage of which will be binocular. Birds see

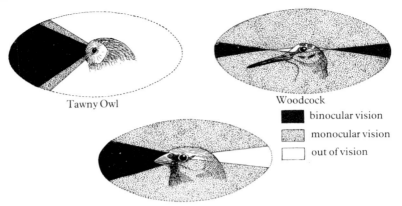

Angle of vision in birds   House Sparrow

The Woodcock can watch for possible enemies through 360° which is very
necessary when its beak is probing deeply in the ground. Raptors have
binocular vision which allows them to judge distances more accurately.

colour in essentially the same way as human beings but they also have an
adaptation which may help to improve their vision in hazy weather. In
addition to the normal eyelid birds have a nictitating membrane which acts
as a third transparent eyelid and is drawn horizontally across the eye from
the nasal-side backwards. It can clean or moisten the surface of the eye
without shutting out the light. In waterbirds such as ducks, divers, and
waders which use their eyes under water this clear window-like lens is so
refractive that it bends the light rays even under water.

Hearing Birds depend on their sense of hearing for keeping in touch with
other members of the flock or their family, for hearing alarm calls or in some
cases even hearing their prey. Apparently some of the plovers can actually
listen to earthworms; the Barn Owl can apparently locate its prey by sound
alone. Birds have a similar range of hearing to human beings – from 20 to
20,000 cycles per second. They can hear sounds that are too rapid for us
to hear. An examination of a sonagram suggests that birds can extract more
information than a human listener. They can automatically locate sounds
by assessing the time-lag between its arrival at either side of the head. It is
also easier to locate the origin of brief sounds rather than long drawn out
ones which is probably why the alarm calls for many species are long
drawn-out whistles or other sounds.

Smell, taste and touch These senses are of little value to birds since their
eyes are so strongly developed. Some species may be able to smell food
while it is in their mouth and this ability can cause some birds to spit out
food which is tainted or obnoxious, such as ants. Taste and touch are
generally poorly developed as well – indeed it is not well known what birds
can taste. The sense of touch is much the same as man's. However, birds do

have special nerve-endings which appear to be particularly sensitive to vibrations such as the shaking of their perch. Waders have sensitive tips to their beaks which allows them to detect their unseen prey. It is also thought that the rictal bristles around the mouth of flycatchers and Nightjars, which are modified feathers, may not only help the bird to catch food but may also be sensitive to vibrations caused by their prey.

Behaviour The study of bird behaviour involves the study of a bird's reactions to objects and situations it meets in everyday life. It is easy to see what a bird is doing but you have to be very careful about interpreting what you see. Quite often bird-lovers try to interpret the behaviour into human terms. You often hear people saying that a Robin or thrush is a devoted mother or that a Robin is happy because he is singing. However, the people who make these remarks fail to realize how complicated the human mind is compared to that of the bird, and how much of their behaviour is instinctive and the result of a little learning.

Most behaviour patterns are instinctive and are performed without any preliminary experience or learning. From the moment that a bird in its egg starts to cut its way out, or to stretch up its head in the nest and open its beak, it is acting instinctively. It knows when to migrate, where to migrate to and in the following year how to build a nest and reproduce. All these instincts connected with reproduction, feeding and migration are inherited and whilst this innate behaviour usually serves the bird well, almost all these activities can be improved as the bird learns through experience. Although since the bird has a small brain its capacity to learn is limited. Instinct, therefore, is the inherited or innate tendency to act in a certain way in response to a certain situation. The behaviour pattern is almost as stereotyped and as flexible as is the innate tendency for an animal to be of a certain size, shape or colour. The basic 'themes' of bird song are instinctive. Most young birds act instinctively to the alarm notes of the parents, even when the parent may have different alarm notes for different dangers.

This instinct generally helps the individual to survive; innate behaviour comes from survivors and generally will be passed on further. Innate behaviour usually occurs in somewhat stereotyped patterns which are called, fixed behaviour patterns. They are very constant in form, and are triggered by stimuli around them which Konrad Lorenz called releasers. However, for various reasons, birds normally only react to any one of these stimuli at appropriate moments. Even so, releasers will not trigger off fixed behaviour patterns until the bird has been motivated; a specific motivation is often called a drive. Thus a bird which is motivated by hunger is probably highly responsive to food stimuli and so on.

I think I should try at this point to bring some of these technical terms to life. Going back to the concept of releasers, in spring it is fairly easy to see how a Robin's red breast triggers off aggressive activities in other Robins defending their territories. Exposure of the white rump of Bullfinches or the white outer tail feathers of a Chaffinch, trigger off flight in other Bullfinches or Chaffinches feeding close by. The red patch on the Herring

Gull's bill is the releaser that will trigger off the feeding behaviour pattern of begging for food by a young bird activated by the hunger drive.

In adults, a build-up towards the activation of an innate behaviour pattern towards a specific goal involves exploratory activities which are technically known as appetitive behaviour. For instance, in the early stages of nest-building birds will often pick up pieces of nest material, play with them in their bills for a while and then drop them. As the drive develops the birds will finally select a nest site and begin to build, picking up and finally inserting a piece of material into the nest, in what is called the consummatory act.

Birds are subject to many different drives every day but normally only one or other of them can be dominant at any particular time. The intensity of a drive may depend on many factors both internally and externally.

Derived from these fixed behaviour patterns are a number of other activities: for instance, at certain times of stress a bird or animal may perform a behaviour pattern entirely out of context. This often occurs when there is a conflict between different drives. When two birds, for example, are displaying to each other in an attempt to establish a territory a conflict may occur between the drive for fighting and the drive to escape. These two drives are incompatible. As neither can be discharged through its normal consummatory act the tension within the bird may find release in irrelevant behaviour and one or both may start preening or picking up nest material, bill-wiping, bathing, false brooding of young or pretending to sleep. These are all outlets through which the thwarted drives can express themselves in some form of motion, and are called displacement activities.

Intention movements are a second type of derived activity. They represent the initial phase of some appetitive behaviour and differ from displacement activities in that they are caused by the drive of their own behaviour patterns but are only of low intensity. One of the most obvious intention movements, which anyone can see, occurs when a bird prepares to fly or when it is disturbed by somebody or an enemy some distance away. Before the bird actually flies it may bend its legs, take the wings away from its body feathers and raise its tail.

A third type of derived activity is known as a redirected activity. This is directed towards an object or animal other than the one releasing it, although the actual releasing object or animal is available as a target at the time. For instance, in a territorial battle the owning bird stops attacking the intruder and begins pecking vigorously at the ground. Quite often Wheatears that I have studied would peck at the ground and tear up grass excitedly in a manner quite different from the way they collected nest material. On one occasion, on Skokholm, one of the bigger, so-called, Greenland Wheatears established its own small territory within the breeding territory of a pair of Wheatears close to their nest. The resident male attacked the larger intruder fairly continuously for a day or so and then gave up. From that moment onwards his own mate attacked him constantly and gave up collecting nest material and building her own nest, until after three or four days the bigger Wheatear moved on.

Learning So far I have been attempting to describe some simple aspects of instinctive behaviour but birds are capable of a little learning. This has been defined by Professor W. H. Thorpe as 'the process which manifests itself by adaptive changes in individual behaviour as a result of experience'. Professor Thorpe's book *Learning and Instinct in Animals* published by Methuen, although very largely about birds covers the whole animal field and for a beginner is somewhat technical. He classifies the types of learning into six main headings: habituation, two types of conditioned reflex learning, latent learning, insight learning and imprinting. In habituation, the instinctive response to a mild and relatively simple stimulus, especially one which warns of danger, wanes as the stimulus continues for long periods without unfavourable results. For instance, an ordinary scarecrow may frighten birds from your cabbage patch for a short time but very soon they will learn that the scarecrow does them no harm. Habituation might be said to keep instincts relevant so that they become more useful.

The term conditioned reflex is usually associated with the Russian physiologist I. P. Pavlov. In the first type of conditioned reflex, an animal learns to respond to a new stimulus for some form of reward. Birds learn to avoid black and orange cinnamon caterpillars after one or two attempts to eat them have revealed their bitter taste. The second type of conditioned reflex is the trial and error type. A young bird may be searching for food and by chance it discovers in pecking at various objects rather haphazardly something which is edible and therefore there is a greater tendency to peck at similar-looking objects. An older bird may learn that an adequate source of food has become available and watches for it to appear. Professor Thorpe mentions the Greenfinch's habit of watching for *Daphne mezereum* berries.

Professor Thorpe defines latent learning as the association of indifferent stimuli or situations without an obvious reward. Perhaps an example of this is the bird's initial exploration of its territory and habitat when it first returns in spring. It learns where there is food and shelter and perhaps, in some cases, where there are potential nest sites. The bird is really taking notice of what is going on in its environment.

The next type is insight learning. It is thought that birds and higher animals can form ideas and use reason which enables them to solve problems very rapidly. Insight learning involves the production of a new adaptive response as a result of insight which indicates an appreciation or apprehension of the relationships of various objects.

Imprinting usually concerns learning in young animals at a highly sensitive period in their development, when they are receiving the first stimuli from the outside world. Konrad Lorenz argued that during a brief period after a bird has hatched the image of a bird's parents or an object that meets its eye in this period is imprinted on the bird's mind so that it will always know its own species. In a classic experiment geese which were hatched from artificially incubated eggs accepted Lorenz and his workers as their parents and followed them as they would have followed their parents.

Migration and ringing

While migration occurs in other animal groups it is most pronounced in birds. Broadly speaking, bird migration is a regular movement between the breeding areas and those which are best suited to feeding needs at other times of the year. There has been much discussion as to the origin and significance of migration. However, it is generally agreed that it enables birds to exploit food that would otherwise be unavailable. Also young can be reared in areas that provide sufficient food in the appropriate season but which may be very inhospitable at other times of the year. Since most northern species breed during the summer months migration takes place in the spring and autumn. It is possible that this type of migration may have evolved after the last glaciation in response to the climatic changes which occurred.

Living as we do in the northern hemisphere we tend to think of it as 'home' for migrants returning from the south. However, having recently spent a winter in a warmer and more southerly part, just north of the equator, where many northern migrants were 'wintering', I tended to take a rather different viewpoint. Many of our summer migrants, which are primarily insect-eaters, spend an average of only four to five months with us. Swifts may remain for as little as three and a half to four months and Spotted Flycatchers and others for about four months. So that for the greater part of the year they are either travelling or in their winter quarters.

Most birds are migratory to some degree. There is every gradation between really sedentary species and those, like the Arctic Tern, which travels some 18,000 kilometres from the Arctic Circle to the Antarctic. Some birds may only make a purely local movement during the winter months like the adult Greenfinches which wander around within a few kilometres of where they normally nest, although young Greenfinches can travel several hundred kilometres.

The classic long-distance migrant is the Swallow. It breeds over much of the northern hemisphere and those from temperate Europe winter south of the Sahara in Africa, often retaining their geographical grouping. The British population concentrates on the moist south-east region of South Africa. The timing of the Swallow's arrival in Britain probably depends upon the availability of certain types of flying insects. The Swallow has always attracted attention and for generations its return has heralded the spring, even in the days when it was thought to hibernate under water. It is a day-migrant and its movements are so obvious that we can trace them

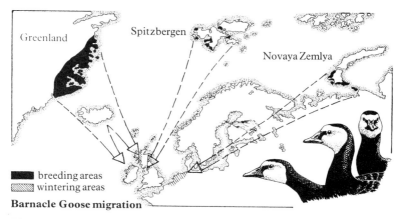

Barnacle Goose migration

The three geographical races of the Barnacle Goose not only breed in different localities but do not even mix when they are in their winter quarters even though they may be less than a hundred kilometres apart.

northwards in spring and southwards in autumn from the records which are kept by many people all over Europe. Peter Davis showed, in 1965, that the main direction of the autumn passage of Swallows through Britain lies to the south-east and south – a direction which generally leads them to the shorter Channel sea-crossing and avoids the longer crossing towards Spain. This direction is maintained into Europe, but some apparently turn south or south-south-west after reaching north France. Like so many other species which winter south of the Sahara or Libyan desert most Swallows cross the thousand or so kilometres of the western Sahara.

On their return northwards Peter Davis's analysis of the Swallow-ringing recoveries indicate that they tend to retrace the path of their autumn migration although the final stages of the spring return may pass further north and east to Belgium and the Netherlands and the final direction of the spring movement into Britain and within Britain is mainly to the north-west and northwards. Indeed, in west Cambridgeshire my own rather limited observations show Swallows crossing my village in a southerly direction in autumn, which leads them to the shortest sea crossing. In spring they travel in a northerly to north-westerly direction. Sometimes geographical factors can divert these birds from their preferred direction. A study of Swallows and other day migrants in your area could show how local geographical factors affect the direction of their flight.

Many different species of birds such as Redwings and Fieldfares which breed to the north and east of us winter in the British Isles unless the weather is so hard that ice and snow cover the land. Then the birds are forced to fly yet further south and west in search of food. Other species use Britain as a staging post, and many of our estuaries are used in this way by waders from the north. The Barnacle Goose which winters here is interesting in that it has three populations which have quite distinct breeding and wintering areas: the Greenland population winters on the north-west coasts of Scotland and Ireland; the Spitzbergen population winters in the Solway and the Russian population in the Netherlands. There is no evidence of any large-scale mixing, even in their winter quarters which may be as little as a hundred kilometres apart (page 91).

How do the birds which undertake these long migrations know where to go and when they should return? Although orientation and navigation in birds has been much studied recently, the answer is still unclear but it is known that birds find their way by a form of compass navigation.

In an experiment to determine how birds navigate a German scientist placed birds in an octagonal cage with a window in each of its sides. During the autumn migration period he counted the number of times birds hopped on to perches on each of the eight sides of the cage. In this way he discovered the preferred orientation of the birds if they had been free – for Starlings this was chiefly to the south-west. This is known as the primary or standard direction. To test the validity of the results he fixed mirrors to the windows in order to change the apparent direction of the sun. As a result the Starlings hopped on to perches on what was now the apparent south-western side.

Dr Geoffrey Matthews went further and showed that birds were apparently able to navigate by using the sun's position combined with an innate sense of time. Experimenting with Manx Shearwaters on the island of Skokholm, he was able to show that birds released in areas in which it was unlikely to have any prior knowledge were, when the sun was shining, able to orientate themselves rapidly in the direction of Skokholm. When the sun was obscured the birds headed out in random directions and took much longer to return. There has been much argument over the years about the rôle of the Earth's magnetic forces in the orientation of birds, and there is still no consensus of opinion.

Much of Dr Matthews' work was done with birds making use of sunlight. However, it is also thought that many of the night migrants can orientate by the stars. Problems arise when stars are obscured in the course of a migratory flight. Radar observations have shown that it is possible for birds to continue on their line even though the stars have been obscured by cloud. If, however, strong winds arise the birds may then become completely disorientated and be blown off course. This results in what the late Kenneth Williamson described as 'drift migration'. In autumn, for instance, birds may begin their autumn flight in a south-westerly direction under anti-cyclonic conditions with a clear sky. Should they meet cyclonic conditions with strong winds and overcast skies they may lose all points of reference and drift down wind. It is this sort of drift which often results in the exciting migrants turning up on the coasts of Britain.

Seabirds, like landbirds, migrate in order to avoid the scarcity of food. Some birds such as gulls, Razorbills and Guillemots, spend most of the

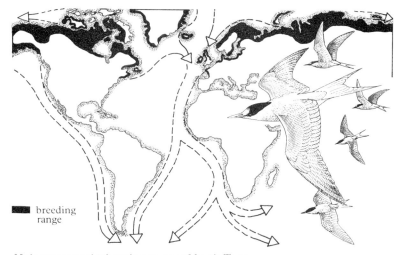

Major autumnal migration routes of Arctic Tern
The migration of the Arctic Tern is one of the longest in the world. Some birds nest within the Arctic Circle and winter within the Antarctic Circle along the edge of the ice.

breeding range

winter on the continental shelf, while others like albatrosses and Puffins roam far out to sea. Some species seem to have a fairly definite wintering area but the movement of other species such as Little Auks, and petrels are little known and may be affected by the wind direction and strength.

To take a few examples, Herring Gulls, during the winter, wander locally around the coast of Britain, probably not travelling more than 2–300 kilometres from their nesting areas. On the east coast the numbers of local birds may be swollen by visitors from north-western Europe. On the other hand the Lesser Black-backed Gull, which is closely related to the Herring Gull, is chiefly a summer visitor to Britain and in winter travels to the western Mediterranean and the Atlantic as well as Europe and Africa as far south as Nigeria.

The most remarkable migration is that of the Arctic Tern. It nests along the north coasts of Europe, Asia and North America and spends our winter in the southern Atlantic and in the Pacific and occasionally even below the Antarctic Circle. The American breeding population crosses the Atlantic in autumn before turning south and then moves down the eastern half of the Atlantic, having joined up with the northern European population. Finally, some of these birds reach the Antarctic pack-ice and spread out along its edge.

The Manx Shearwater, which was originally studied by R. M. Lockley on his island home in Pembrokeshire, is also a great traveller in winter, and ringed birds have been discovered along the South American coast as well

93

as in Australia, but the complete story of its winter movements is still to be discovered. Of course, many seabirds, and particularly the auks and their young, swim quite long distances in the autumn when they leave their breeding quarters.

What you, the naturalist, see of migration depends on many factors, especially the geography of the area in which you live. If you look at maps in some bird books which show the directions which migrants are said to take, you might think that they follow rather narrow routes, perhaps down the coasts of Britain and Europe, although we have seen that there is a tendency for Swallows to do this. But observations by radar have shown that, providing there are no impediments, migrants generally travel in primary or standard directions on a broad front across the country, although quite often rivers, hills, woods and coastlines deflect them in other directions, sometimes even in the opposite direction to the primary one. Many species such as the Wheatear, for instance, on their way from Africa to Alaska, must obviously change their primary direction on different parts of their routes. In western Europe the primary direction of most birds is south-westerly or southerly which takes them clear of the high mass of the Alps and towards the shorter sea crossing of the Iberian peninsula. In eastern Europe the primary direction of many species is to the south-east.

The Red-backed Shrike is famous for its 'loop' migration. R. E. Moreau, who has made a special study of the trans-Saharan migration of birds, says that it is probable that in autumn the Red-backed Shrike of western Europe travels in an easterly or south-easterly direction until it nears the Aegean Sea when it changes to a southerly direction and crosses the eastern Mediterranean. In the return spring passage the shrikes leave Africa some 1000 kilometres east of where they entered in autumn, coming up north to the east of Suez and through Syria. There has been much discussion as to why they should undertake this migratory route. Moreau suggests that during the rather formidable desert crossing northwards the shrikes take advantage of the south-westerly winds that predominate at high levels and bring them into the eastern corner of the Mediterranean where the winds over the sea are also favourable.

In some parts of northern Europe where, for instance, the coastline of the Netherlands concentrates masses of Starlings, finches and Lapwings moving out of eastern Europe, one can see some huge numbers of birds passing. During one such movement on the shores of the Issjelmeer in the Netherlands, I saw 56,000 Chaffinches and 26,000 Starlings passing over in a matter of four hours. Only very rarely can you see such a volume of migration in Britain as the largest mass of birds from north-east Europe and Scandinavia generally passes to the south of us along its primary south-westerly direction. However, on the west coast of Wales and in one or two other areas, which concentrate birds, you can see some fairly striking movements. Throughout Britain on October and November mornings, shortly after sunrise, it is possible to see Chaffinches and other birds moving in a south-westerly direction.

The first autumn movement in Britain is, perhaps, less obvious than many others, it usually begins about mid-June, when Lapwings, dispersing from their breeding grounds, fly westwards in small flocks. Travelling at the same time may be Curlew and other marshland waders. This is not a migration in the strict sense but more a dispersal of young birds and unsuccessful breeders. They pass over my part of Cambridgeshire and most go further west since, at this time, the cereal has not been harvested and we have little pasture land.

What has emerged from a number of studies of birds' behaviour and movements after the breeding season is that migrants may not stay in one place throughout the winter but perhaps stay for a period of a month or so in one area before passing on to another. Waders may spend several weeks in some estuaries fattening up before moving on to other appropriate habitats further south. It has recently been shown that Pied Flycatchers congregate in the Iberian peninsula for a 'fattening' period where they prepare for the trans-Saharan crossing. We all know that our own Redwings, Fieldfares and, indeed, visiting Blackbirds and Song Thrushes may stay with us in our local fields for a period before they too move on to other parts, sometimes further south if the weather with us is very hard. A great deal depends upon the availability of food as well as the weather and, as a result, birds will travel by different routes in different years.

Hard weather starts off very large movements to the south-west and south. For example, one January, after heavy snowfalls on the Pembroke-shire coast, in a matter of fifteen minutes, I counted 2,600 birds, mostly Starlings, Skylarks and Lapwings, flying westwards towards Ireland. Later in the same day I calculated that in one area of about five square kilometres there must have been over a million birds foraging on the fields. From time to time I have seen, even in Cambridgeshire, smaller movements of birds in westerly directions after substantial falls of snow either to the east or north of us.

In recent years, radar has increased our knowledge about migration and made it clear that we, with our binoculars, only see a fraction of a movement. What we may see on the ground has therefore to be interpreted most carefully. Nevertheless, the local birdwatcher should know the primary or standard direction followed by the common visible day migrants, and try to find out what happens to them as they move through his part of the country and subsequently compare the numbers that he has seen, as well as the directions, with any previous published records. There is still scope for some co-operative efforts amongst members of bird clubs in different parts of Britain to trace what is happening to our local migrants.

Finally, coming to some technical points: in recording the migrations of birds in your notebook, there are a number of things to note. Inevitably, you should record the date, place and time during which the observations took place, as well as the weather conditions, including cloud cover, wind direction and speed according to the Beaufort scale. You can record the flocks as they appear and pass over your observation line. You need to record the species, the number in each flock, direction of flight, height above ground and any calls that they are making. If you have time, try to record comments on any other features that strike you, whether, for instance, the birds continue to fly in the same direction. Is it true, for instance, that Chaffinches, while travelling in their primary direction, tend to head from one wood to the next? It is particularly important if you are near the sea and are watching birds take off over the sea to follow them for as long as you can. Do they change direction after they have gone some distance from land? Do they gain height or go down closer to sea-level? On good days it can happen that the birds are passing in such numbers that you cannot record all the details in full. If you have a miniature tape-recorder you can record your observations and transcribe them later. Failing that you can draw a compass-rose with eight or sixteen points, in your notebook for each species that is passing. To each of the directions you add an arrowhead with the numbers for each flock – it is best to use a new compass-rose every hour or so, or more frequently if required. While this is a quick way of coping with large numbers you do lose some precision. If you visit different locations in your birdwatching area this sort of compass-rose with flight directions marked on, can summarize your observations of the general direction of migration in your area and, perhaps, can show how various geographical features effect the routes.

I used to map the autumn migration of Swallows and Meadow Pipits on Skokholm and later on also, the Skylarks on the Dale Peninsula. The map opposite shows how the coastline leads the migrant Swallows away from their preferred easterly or southerly direction. Migrant Skylarks on the other hand were moving west to Ireland and yet at the same time and in the same place others were apparently flying south-east out of Ireland, probably to move further south. Building up an accurate picture of what is happening to birds within your area is a useful and satisfying occupation, and perhaps one day that knowledge may be required by others.

There is also a need for someone to learn more about migration at night by watching birds flying across the face of the moon. C. J. Henty (*Scottish Birds* 10:2) has recently renewed the interest in this study.

Ringing Although radar has become an extremely useful tool in the study of migration, the marking of a bird with a leg-ring, so that it can be individually recognized, has for a long time been a key method for discovering more about a bird's travels, its life expectancy, its family relationships and so on. The ring is a very light, but strong, band of aluminium or nickel alloy. This band is carefully wrapped around the bird's leg using a special pair of pliers. The ringer makes a note of the ring number, the species of bird and any other facts that he can glean about it, and then sends the most important details to the British Trust for Ornithology which co-ordinates the ringing scheme in Britain. A legend on the ring asks the finder to inform the BTO at Tring directly or the British Museum (Natural History), London, and in their turn they pass the record on to the BTO which has the data as to where the bird was caught, the

The full extent of the Manx Shearwater's winter wanderings in the southern oceans is still unknown; to discover the direction in which its home burrow lies the Shearwater practices a simple form of navigation.

Bird observatories such as that at Portland Bill are established to study migration by ringing and recording weights, etc. of birds which have been caught in Heligoland traps and mist nets. Most bird observatories welcome voluntary help.

97

Above Ruffs, so-called because of the necklace of coloured feathers, occupy small territories known as leks. When Reeves, the females, appear at the lek they approach a male and copulation takes place. The females then go off on their own to rear the family.

Left This photograph shows the Robin in a posture commonly seen in spring where, by stretching up its head, it is showing off the full length of its red breast and throat to an intruder.

Right The young of Greenshank are nidifugous and they leave the nest within hours of hatching but keep together as a family even when they can fly. The young are cryptically coloured.

Below The young of these Buzzards are nidicolous and remain in the nest while the early stages of their growth are completed. Only when food is exceptionally abundant are all the young reared.

The Red-backed Shrike's range has contracted markedly in Britain and western Europe over the last hundred years possibly linked with the cooler and wetter summers.

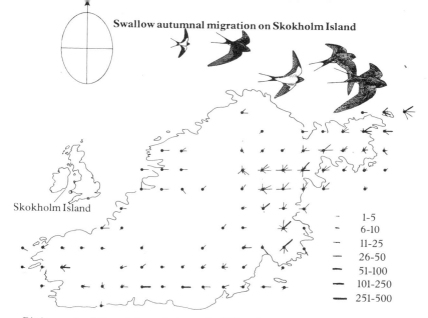

Swallow autumnal migration on Skokholm Island

Skokholm Island

—	1-5
—	6-10
—	11-25
—	26-50
—	51-100
—	101-250
—	251-500

Birds may be deflected from their standard direction of migration by geographical features. This study of migrant Swallows crossing Skokholm shows how the coastline forced them northwards.

number of times it has been caught, and how long it has lived. Details of each recovery are sent back to the finder and to the original ringer so that he too can build up a life history. The story that results may be that a Robin, which has been recovered many times before, is still living in a village four years after it was originally caught, or that a Wheatear that was ringed on Skokholm at 1 pm on the 16th of August was shot at 8 am at Cap Breton, Landes, France on the 18th of August over 936 kilometres away, 43 hours later. The Protection of Birds Act 1967, prohibits ringing except under licence issued by the Nature Conservancy Council through the British Trust for Ornithology. Furthermore, certain methods for trapping birds as well as attempting to trap certain rare birds in their breeding areas requires an additional licence. The BTO publish a very useful account of what ringing has achieved, the BTO Guide No. 16 entitled, *Bird Ringing* by Chris Mead.

Birds can be caught in a variety of different ways. Some bird observatories, usually located on islands and peninsulars around the coast of Britain, still operate the 'Heligoland' trap. This is a huge funnel-shape construction covered in wire netting, which, as its name suggests, was originally developed on the island of Heligoland. The entrance to the funnel is open and is usually planted with shrubs which attract the

Rocket nets being used to catch Oystercatchers at high tide on a field beside The Wash, Norfolk. This method of netting has been used to ring large numbers of geese, ducks and waders without harming them. It is hoped that in time this ringing will enable us to have a better understanding of the movements of these birds.

migrants. The birds are driven from these bushes up the narrowing funnel and finally into a small catching box from which they can be easily removed. A second method of catching birds, which has been used for generations, is netting. The old nets were made of cotton and had a number of drawbacks. The use of nylon has made it possible to construct nets with threads so fine that they are difficult to see when set in front of trees and bushes. Because of this quality they have acquired the name 'mist' nets. They are extremely effective and in the wrong hands would do so much damage to birds that it is now necessary to obtain a licence to use them. Many ringers, particularly those working on a population of a particular area, ring nestlings.

Nestlings, again, need considerable care when handling and a ringer has to obtain an additional licence. The advantage of ringing nestlings is that whenever one is recaptured, its exact age will be known.

The ringing of more elusive birds such as geese and waders has been carried out by the use of rocket nets which were developed successfully in Britain in the early 1960s by The Wildfowl Trust, Slimbridge. The method involves careful positioning of nets powered by rockets in high-tide roosting areas as well as attracting birds to the correct position for netting either by the use of decoys or careful shepherding from a distance.

In addition to the numbered rings there are other ways in which birds may be marked to make them recognizable as individuals. Some scientists mark the birds they are studying with wing-tags which are usually brightly coloured plastic tags. They are fitted to the forewing in such a way that they lie flat over the wing and do not impede the bird's progress. Numbers written on them, together with the colours of the tag, enable the bird to be individually identified from some distance. They are safe if properly used but are unsightly – I can always remember seeing Jackdaws flying in to land from Skomer with what looked like orange headlamps attached to their wings.

When I lived on Skokholm and studied the life history of the Wheatear, I wanted to learn as much as possible about the population. I therefore ringed as many Wheatears as possible not only with the BTO ring but also with three coloured plastic rings – two on one leg and one with the aluminium ring on the other leg. Each bird had a unique combination of colours so that I was able to recognize the individual, using telescope or binoculars, by checking on the combination. I learned a little about the migration of Wheatears – not many are recovered in their winter quarters – but I discovered that individual Wheatears will return year after year to the same territory, even to the same nest hole if the old nest has been cleared away, and even to the same mate if it has returned as well. I also learned something about their occasional bigamy; how the young dispersed after they left the nest; how many of the young returned to the island the following year to breed and with whom they mated. I learned how long some of them lived – one of my Wheatears was five years old and I would probably have found others of a greater age had I been able to remain longer on the island.

In the early days when there were few ringers, most of the birds were recovered dead but as more ringers took part in the scheme and worked on populations of birds in their area so the numbers of live recoveries increased and now each re-trap or 'control' of a live bird ringed by someone else adds another fact to that bird's life history.

In addition to the story of migration and family and social relationship one also obtains much information about other facts of a bird's life. The booklet *Bird Ringing* lists, for instance, the maximum age of a number of birds as shown by ringing recoveries. I have extracted some which seemed to me to be of particular interest.

Maximum ages of some birds shown by ringing recoveries:

Manx Shearwater	20 years old	Great Tit	10 years old
Gannet	16	Blue Tit	11
Heron	18	Wren	5
Mallard	14	Song Thrush	9
Mute Swan	15	Blackbird	12
Kestrel	14	Robin	8
Moorhen	10	Willow Warbler	5
Common Tern	25	Starling	13
Arctic Tern	27	Chaffinch	10
Woodpigeon	15	House Sparrow	10
Rook	15		

Ringing has shown that young Fulmars leave their ledges when they are about seven weeks old. They spend the next three or four years at sea before they finally return to the cliffs to prospect for nest sites for several seasons. Only then do they begin to breed, in about their seventh year. Their mean expectation of life is about sixteen years, but they have a potential life span of fifty years. Dr David Lack has calculated that the average further life (life after its first year) for an adult songbird is 1–2 years, for various waders and gulls 2–3 years, and for Swifts 4–5 years.

The ringing recovery of a species of which fairly large numbers have been ringed can give interesting information about life expectation, mortality rate, etc. The mortality rate of some birds is very high but is balanced by a high rate of breeding. Chris Mead in his booklet points out that if only one young survives from each pair's breeding activity each year the Robin population would increase by more than 50 times every 10 years. Chris Mead also calculated the annual mortality for three common species: 35% for the Blackbird, 53% for the Starling and 44% for the House Sparrow. Two larger species for which figures have been worked out are 15% for the Herring Gull and 6% annual mortality for the breeding population of Fulmars in Scotland.

Some people worry that ringing or the actual wearing of a ring is cruel to birds and that they might be damaged when they are being caught or that the weight of the ring will hinder their feeding. As I indicated earlier, every ringer in Britain has to undergo a strict training programme before he is allowed to ring on his own and while accidents can always happen most ringers now operate with a strong sense of their own responsibility. The rings are very light in weight and should fit fairly snugly; even when I used an aluminium ring and three plastic rings on Wheatears, the total combined weight was, relatively speaking, less than one shoe on a human being or less than the daily variation in a Wheatear's body weight: the Wheatear puts on weight as it feeds during the day and loses it during the night. There really is, generally speaking, no evidence that ringing harms birds. Furthermore, the table of longevity shows that ringed birds are able to survive to a good age. In addition some of the knowledge gained which has been used in public enquiries has benefitted whole populations of birds.

Territory, song and courtship

If you are watching almost any aspect of a bird's breeding biology and behaviour and, indeed, sometimes its winter behaviour, sooner or later, you need to understand the part that territory plays in its life. Although Aristotle made some reference to the territory of eagles and a number of other writers have since commented on the fact that many breeding males cannot tolerate the presence of another male close to them, it was a businessman and amateur ornithologist, Eliot Howard, who first developed the idea of territory in his book, *Territory in Bird Life*. Since then territory has attracted the attention of birdwatchers from amateurs to highly erudite scientists and yet, there are still points of interpretation on which there is no agreement. Indeed, there remain species, even common ones, whose territories have never been studied in detail. So there is room for birdwatchers, not only to learn for themselves about territory and all its ramifications, but perhaps to add something new to science.

No single definition of territory covers all its different manifestations. Probably the simplest and most generally accepted definition at present is, 'any defended area', but even that has some drawbacks as a definition, because a pair may occupy a territory and 'enjoy' its benefits but may never have to defend it, as they may not have any others of the same species close enough to defend it from.

Nowadays, there are generally considered to be six or seven types of territory: the first is a mating, nesting and feeding territory, which is the type of territory occupied by Robins, Wrens, Blackbirds and Wheatears. The second type is a mating and nesting territory, here, a typical bird is the Goldfinch which leaves its territory in order to find food. The third type of territory is the mating territory, and the leks of Ruffs and Blackcocks are good examples of this. The fourth type is a simple nesting territory and here we think of the seabird in their dense colonies. The fifth type is a feeding territory but there really is not much evidence about this; whether it is really a territory, in the strict sense, or a form of 'individual distance' is open to debate. 'Individual distance' is an area about one body length around a bird and which moves with the bird; although it has no visible boundaries it is defended. It would be interesting to know how closely related this type of territory is to the sixth type, the so-called winter territory, which several species hold during the winter months. In Britain a notable example of a species which holds this type of territory is the Robin. However, a number of migratory species, for example, Wheatears and

Thousands of Starlings roost in the centres of cities in Britain where the night temperature is often higher than in woods. Notice how regularly they space themselves; this is their 'individual distance'.

shrikes hold territories in their winter quarters, and also on migration. Some of the leaf warblers seem to have at least temporarily restricted territories in their winter quarters and, perhaps, whenever they rest on migration.

This type of territory could also be linked with the seventh type – the roosting territory. For instance, Starlings are known to return to the same perch to roost at night and to defend the spot. Treecreepers return to the same hollow in the soft bark of Redwood trees and attack other Treecreepers which come close to it. While the first four types of territory seem to be fairly straightforward, I have some unease about the ordering and nomenclature of the last three groups. The Reverend E. A. Armstrong differentiates between territory used for reproductive purposes and those used for self-preservation. This seems to be a logical split between the first four types and the last three.

The function of territory varies enormously between species and in addition to the important function of restricting disturbance to a breeding pair, territory also spaces out birds and allows individuals to become attached for a while to a particular site.

The size of the territory varies, not only between species but also within species. The size of the breeding territory of Razorbills, or other seabirds may be as little as 0.3 square metres around the nest or egg; where the territory is a nesting and mating area it may be slightly larger. The

Goldfinches which I studied when I was a prisoner-of-war had territories which averaged 250 square metres when they were building the nest and courting vigorously. However, once they were engaged in feeding the young the size of the territory dwindled to between 9 and 12 square metres although as the nest was up a tree it would perhaps be more accurate to say about 20 cubic metres around the nest. The territories of Pheasants also decrease in size as the breeding season progresses. There may also be reasons for size differences of individual territories depending on availability of nest-sites and so on.

If a pair of birds has to find food, mate and nest in the same territory, as well as bringing up their young, the size is even greater. The territory of the Wheatear on Skokholm varied between 0·49 hectares and 3·28 hectares, averaging 1·54 hectares. Professor Hinde has listed the average territory size for four species of tits. The 14 territories of Great Tits that he measured averaged 0·8 hectares; the three territories of Blue Tits covered 0·2, 0·4 and 0·8 hectares; the three territories of Marsh Tits covered 1·8, 1·5 and 2·2 hectares; and the territories of two pairs of Willow Tits both covered about 8 hectares. In Cambridge, the territory of male Wrens who were unrestrained by rivals in neighbouring territories patrolled over 2·4–2·8 hectares, whereas elsewhere Wren territory size could be as low as 0·4 hectares.

Not all birds of prey have territories and, as Leslie Brown points out, for most species, 'home range' is a better term. Buzzards have territories which they defend but Kestrels do not. Golden Eagles may be dispersed 5 or 6 kilometres apart and the area which may be available for each pair to range over may be between 39 and 60 square kilometres.

Normally the males defend their territories – they sing and proclaim their presence. Generally they are also more brightly coloured than the females and these colours are often used in displays. The males attack both male and female intruders, particularly when the male is unmated. Once, however, a pair occupy a territory, a female will approach another intruding female and see her off. As the female does not usually have the bright colours of the male she does not normally use the same posturing, so their routine is a dominance display followed by a chase; if the intruding female does not retreat, then a fight ensues.

The type of habitat, population density and the individual aggressiveness of the owner (these last two factors may be linked), leads to variations in territory size. Indeed, in a way, individual aggressiveness is probably the important factor in the variation of territory size. It would seem that while the shortage of food within a habitat may occasionally be responsible for a low population, the chief way in which a habitat affects population is its ability to screen the view of one aggressive male from another. The territories of the Skokholm Wheatears were much smaller – about 0·8 hectares in the rocky south-east part of the island near Spy Rock – than on the more open northern plains where they could cover as much as 3 hectares. The reason for this was, I believe, that the broken ground prevented neighbouring males from seeing each other. Carl Welty, in his *Life of Birds*, mentions that foliage density is also important, because it reduces the chances of one owner seeing another. As I have mentioned in the section on habitat, the distance the bird can see can affect its behaviour in a number of ways that would not appear to have been studied yet, both in relation to habitat selection and size of territory.

Variation of population density in waterbirds such as the Great Crested Grebe is a well known factor affecting territory size. The less successful pairs of some species in terrestrial, rather than aquatic habitats, will move to less suitable ground when the population density is high and there will be a little reduction in territory size. The territories of Robins and many other species are also compressible in response to population pressure and there can also be seasonal changes in area, too. There does not seem to be any direct evidence that territory limits the total breeding population in all habitats. However, where there is clearly a dense population of birds already, the chances that a latecomer will be able to carve a territory out for himself are fairly small.

Whilst keeping an area free of intruders is one important characteristic of territory, another is site attachment. A male and female will for part of the year become attached to, and isolated in, one particular part of a habitat which they will often defend. This is thought to have many advantages: it has been suggested that for some species territory is important in the formation and maintenance of the bond between the pair. Philip Brown and Gwen Davies, who studied the Reed Warbler, emphasize that the female wandered about rather widely when she first arrived and that, therefore, the male's territory must be large enough to contain her. Ruffs and Blackcocks only use part of their territory or 'lek' for the display in which they indulge, and once the female has been fertilized and has laid her eggs it is abandoned. In a few species, territory may be important in ensuring a food supply for the young. Indeed, the territories of some hummingbirds are centred on a food supply, but it is clear that generally, this is of little importance.

An attachment to one site is also important in another sense: the owners gain familiarity – particularly if they return year after year – with places where food is available or where shelter can be found. This, for example, increases their 'confidence', to use a very anthropomorphic term; an older Wheatear which had bred successfully in one year was able, when it returned rather late to Skokholm, to dislodge a younger Wheatear, which had already established itself in the territory occupied by the older bird in the previous year.

Some Wheatears live until they are five years old and perhaps longer. In spring they usually return to the same territory and pair with the same mate if it has also returned. I came to the conclusion that familiarity with a previous year's mate was also useful. However, although Wheatears tended to be faithful to a mate, the evidence really showed that they were more faithful to the territory. At the end of each breeding season they would part, and disperse independently from the nest area.

Stone-curlews are territorial in the breeding season but in the autumn they gather in flocks before migrating. Here two birds are displaying aggressively with their necks stretched and tails spread.

Dr David Lack, in his book *Swifts in a Tower*, tells how Swifts return to a previous nest site and if the previous year's mate returns then the bond is reformed. Several species as different as Bearded Tits and ducks form pairs as many as six months before they actually nest. In spite of this betrothal period they split and go their own ways at the end of the nesting period. Jackdaws may be one of the few species where the evidence suggests that they mate for life.

Some of the more obvious manifestations of territory are song and the various display patterns which birds use to defend their territory. These manifestations enable us to determine where the boundaries of the territories are, how large they are and what uses pairs make of them. Most male birds advertise their presence by a song which identifies their species, their sex and their sexuality. Also, there is a tendency to attack individuals which intrude in the territory and, if they leave their own territory, a tendency to flee from other birds that attack them.

The song is usually loud and often delivered from a conspicuous perch or during a display flight, such as the 'butterfly flight' of the Greenfinch. Other examples are the song flight of the Skylark, circling over the fields and the tumbling flight of the Whitethroat. The places which are used as song perches are enormously varied and have been studied by Derek Hulme, on his way to work. He showed that only the Starling showed a preference for buildings as song post, while the Wren patronized natural song posts exclusively. This is another study that might be repeated.

The tendency to attack individuals which intrude is usually manifested by a variety of threat displays; actual fighting only occurs when the threats have failed. The most obvious examples are found in our own gardens: each territory owner seems to try to assert his own dominance over the area first by song and then by display. When an intruder comes into a territory the bird, such as a Robin or Blackbird, hops towards it in a somewhat upright position and at first, patrols alongside it. Often this approach is sufficient to make the intruder flee. If, however, this display of dominance does not have the desired effect, the owner will start to adopt various extravagant postures: the Robin, for example, lifts its head and neck and displays its red breast, keeping it towards the intruder, whether the latter is perched above or below. The Blackbird adopts various aggressive postures in an upright position with body and neck feathers fluffed out so that the whole body appears larger, also, the tail is usually depressed and slightly fanned. The Wheatear has a somewhat similar upright position and, like the Robin, shows off its pale sandy buff throat and breast, as well as the black and white markings on the head, wings and tail.

Other birds in similar situations also make use of exaggerated postures and emphasize prominent patches and colour. Great Tits, for instance, have what is called the 'head up posture', which reveals more clearly the black throat and belly markings, the sudden revelation of which is often enough to make an attacker hold off in mid-air.

If these displays fail the owner may eventually fly at the intruder and a chase may ensue. Sometimes the intruder leaves the territory but then tries to come back by another route, in this case the chase is prolonged. Finally, if the owner is still determined to hold on to the territory and the intruder remains reluctant to leave a real fight can ensue, with the birds attempting to peck and fly at each other. Very occasionally, these battles result in the death of one or other of the combatants.

During late winter and early spring, many resident birds begin to show signs of establishing their territories and, for the curious ornithologist, there is a large field for observation and interpretation. Much has been written on the subject of territory and it has occupied the minds of amateur and professional ornithologists alike, particularly just after the war years. But there is still much to be described and interpreted, even for common species.

Song Bird song is a difficult phrase to interpret. Some people argue that it is the wrong term to use in relation to birds, because song is a human art form and, therefore, implies a form of music. Although we may think that many of the sounds that birds make when they are singing are musical – birds themselves do not and cannot appreciate that they are making music. Some specialists talk about the bird vocalizations – even this term produces complications because not all the sounds are vocal. Others use the term 'sound pattern', which is useful because of the difficulty in drawing a line between bird song and bird calls – a difference which is functional rather than musical. In some species, the song is made up of a rapid repetition of its call notes. Song can best be defined as a series of notes or sounds consistently repeated according to some specific pattern. It is produced mainly by the male, and usually during the breeding season. Call notes are usually short sequences of up to four or five notes, often much less musical. They are generally rather brief sounds with a relatively simple acoustic structure.

Both songs and calls convey messages over longer distances than do the postures that a bird adopts when displaying, although the effect of song is sometimes reinforced by displays. Song is not a language in the sense that we understand it – it cannot convey precise instructions but it can convey a feeling.

Whilst song serves a number of functions, some sexual, some social and some individual, the most important function of all is to proclaim the identity and sex of the singer. It also maintains an emotional relationship between the singer and his mate. Some songs and calls are linked with the presence of the young and will convey that information to other species. It has been claimed that certain types of budgerigar song actually induce the female to lay eggs. Finally, song will identify the individual, itself, to its mate and to its offspring because each bird song differs slightly from that of its neighbour.

For the individual bird, song helps to discharge nervous energy and, in spite of implying that everything about song is mechanical, a bird does manage to perfect song through practice and the possibility that some birds sing for the joy of it should not be arbitrarily ruled out.

Birds have a varied vocabulary of calls; some may be, like song, declarations of territorial rights, and be used when the motivation to defend is low. Calls also indicate needs, other than territorial or sexual; for example, the need for company may be one of the functions of the calls of young birds, which are still dependent on their parents. Alarm calls, especially those indicating certain dangers, such as the near approach of a predator, trigger an immediate reaction which may not only affect birds of the same species but others as well. The 'pinking' of a Blackbird when a Tawny Owl is discovered, gives a particularly obvious example of this type of call. Some of the more extreme alarm calls, which give warnings of predators, apparently also indicate fear and tend to be high-pitched with a relatively narrow frequency range and indefinite endings. This gives them an almost ventriloquial effect, making them extremely difficult to locate.

Anybody who has watched tits feeding in woodland areas will know that it is possible to locate the flock by following the contact notes. These contact notes tell each bird where the others are, and warn them off if they are getting too close. At the same time they attract back to the flock birds which have been wandering off. The utterances of some birds communicate not only the location but also the presence of some other object.

A type of song which is much quieter than the normal song of a species is the 'subsong'. One of its characteristics is that the fundamental frequencies are generally lower than in the normal song. It also has a different pattern and is said to be characteristic of lower sexual motivation; some experts say it has no communicative function. I am not certain that we can accept this as the whole truth. In my studies of the Wheatear, for instance, 'subsong' was only used by unmated birds holding a territory, apparently as advertising song. The full song was only used by the unmated bird when it became extremely excited, for example, in a territorial battle. Once the Wheatear was mated it sang the full song and used the song flight. The warbling subsong was then used less often and then only in sexual circumstances. Subsong is also used by females under certain circumstances. In the autumn subsong is often used by young birds of many species and then it is thought to be in the nature of practice. As I have mentioned before some birds, such as Robins, use their full song until they are mated and then more or less stop singing. So we have enormous variations.

Most of the songs I have been writing about so far consist of vocal sounds. However, many advertising sounds made by birds are non-vocal. One of the best known examples is the drumming of the Great and Lesser Spotted Woodpeckers. These sounds are made by a very rapid tattoo of blows by the bill on a dead branch usually near its end. The sound can carry up to 400 metres or more through a wood. This drumming equates with the advertising song in songbirds. The bill clattering of White Storks, which is a greeting display, when one adult throws back its head in recognition of and greeting to its mate, is often shown in bird films.

The use of the wings to produce sounds are well known to the average birdwatcher. They vary from the wing-clapping of the Woodpigeon to the fast tumbling flight of the Lapwing, whose hard-beating wings are able to produce a 'buzzing' sound on the downstroke. Nightjars and some owls also clap their wings noisily as part of their sexual and territorial displays. The 'drumming' or 'bleating' of the Snipe is perhaps the best example of producing sound from the tail feathers. To produce this the Snipe, while flying over its marshland territory, dives at a gentle angle and fans its tail. The outer pair of tail feathers are separated from the remaining six pairs and the sound, which lasts about two seconds, is the result of the air rushing past these feathers and causing them to vibrate.

Few birds sing all the year round and most song is correlated to the breeding season, being partly linked with the increasing length of the day. It usually parallels the growth of the testes. At the turn of the year, many species may resume singing, provided the weather is not too hard. Robins reach their maximum song-output as early as February but most species apparently do not reach it until April or May. The frequency of song falls off when the young hatch. In August, when many birds are moulting, there is little song but later in the autumn singing starts again from Chiffchaffs, Willow Warblers, Wheatears and others and they may even be signs of nesting activities. This may be accounted for, in part, by the autumnal recrudescence of the gonads.

In 1944 P. R. Cox published the results of his investigations into the seasonal course of bird song. It is a model which present day amateurs

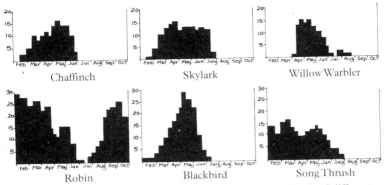

These histograms show the variation in the number of individuals of different species singing during the morning and evening. Is the variation similar in your area? (after P. R. Cox).

might follow, either by repeating Cox's study as to what is the most popular season for song and the most popular time of day for each species, or by trying to find out how often on average other species, which Cox did not study, sing. They could compare their study with Cox's work and those of others and discover whether there have been any significant changes.

Bird song has often moved the hearts and souls of poets and musicians as well as naturalists. To be out early at sunrise and hear the dawn chorus in spring, or to just sit and listen to the bird song in your garden on a summer's evening, can be a thrilling experience, or simply relaxing if you are in a contemplative mood. The birdwatcher may want to go beyond contemplation and ask himself a whole range of questions. What are the times and seasons during which birds sing, and from where do they sing? How does the weather affect song? Does the range of song perches change throughout the season and depend on the amount of foliage? Are they exposed when in song, or hidden? How many different types of song does a male have and what are the occasions on which he uses them? Having started to answer these questions, others will follow. The tape-recordist, too, can capture the different varieties of song and calls and, perhaps, build up, by cutting, editing and resplicing, a sound picture of a typical bird from your garden or favourite habitat.

Pair formation Song tells an unmated female, newly arrived from her winter quarters, of a territory-holding male which is ready for a mate. But when the newly-arrived female comes into a territory she is often attacked as if she is an intruding male, and if she is not ready to mate she may well move on. If, on the other hand, the female holds her ground and does not leave the territory or, as in some species, lowers her head, exposing the nape of her neck in a submissive posture, the male will eventually stop attacking her and accept her as a mate. The females of some species, for instance the Chaffinch and the American Song Sparrow, respond with a special call, when they are prepared to accept the attacking male as a mate. The pair then settle down and initially seek out the boundaries of their territory and discover what it contains in the way of food and shelter. Indeed, one gets the impression from watching newly paired Wheatears that they are learning not only about their territory but also about each other.

Once the birds are paired they will usually remain so until the end of the breeding season and then return to their wintering areas independently. Amongst some species which raise two broods, the female will occasionally take a new mate for the second, if the first male has started his moult and has deserted her. In the Wheatear this led to polygamy: the female which had been deserted formed a pair with a neighbouring male which had not deserted his territory or mate. Not all birds pair for the season; the male and female Ruff and Blackcock meet at the lek, copulate there and part, and the male takes no further interest in the female, eggs or young, so this must be one of the shortest pairings.

Birds which mate in the flock in winter follow a rather different pattern from those where migrant males set up their territory. Pairing up in a flock which may be moving from place to place is a bit more difficult to study and there are few details about this type of pair formation. Ian Newton, whose book entitled *Finches* which is already a classic study, says that the act of forming pairs is a less definite affair than in territorial species because the relationship between the two birds develops over several days or weeks and is not marked by any particular event. Cock Greenfinches become more aggressive towards other cocks in the flock and begin to relinquish their dominance over females. They court them by crouching in a special posture and reaching out and attempting to touch or nibble at their bills. Gradually, as time passes, the pairs are drawn closer together and the hen assumes dominance from the male, finally leading the cock in search of nest sites.

Courtship displays Whilst song is one way of manifesting sexual feelings, courtship displays are another. In some species they may reinforce the effect of song but in others they are the main method by which the male communicates to the female his need to mate with her.

During these courtship displays the males demonstrate patches of bright colours to their mates by twisting themselves into odd and sometimes fantastic positions. Some of this colour may often remain concealed until the bird takes up this posture. Other patches of colour are only revealed when the tips of the dull autumn feathers, which helped to camouflage the birds during the winter, wear off. Some plumages used in displays are grown every spring between January and April, like the plumes of the Great White and Little Egret, as well as the variously coloured necklet feathers of the Ruff. Not only feathers but other parts of the body are used in displays; certain areas of skin, such as the brilliant red-skinned throat pouches of the frigatebirds of the tropical seas, are inflated during their display. Puffins grow their large and multi-coloured bills just before they return to their nesting slopes, and some of the herons, and in particular the

Little Bittern, can change its bill colour quite quickly when the male encounters the female at the nest.

The courtship displays have a number of important functions. They stimulate sexual readiness, sometimes not only in the bird being courted but also in the bird doing the courting. Often seabirds nesting on cliff-face colonies will not have such a wide range of sexual displays as, for instance, smaller song birds and a number of social displays appear to compensate for this. These large social displays, such as the head-flicking or hiccuping of the Puffins, may also stimulate sexual readiness, not only in their own mates but in other members of the colony. At a seabird colony in the evening you may often see three-quarters of the Puffin colony on a clifftop head-flicking as though they all have hiccups.

Amongst the many displays are those in which the male brings material to the nest, usually with excitement and sometimes with some ceremony. Gulls, terns, gannets, herons and indeed many passerines all bring material and may display it with some excitement to the female. I have even seen cock Goldfinches and Wheatears, which do not normally build, occasionally bring material to their nests, but they did not always persevere with attempts to weave in the material; often these small offerings were dropped or carried away again.

Most of the true courtship displays, therefore, bring birds towards the fertilization of the female. Day length and temperature have already affected their sex organs and the pair have sought out their special area for breeding which will bring the maximum quantity of food for the young birds when they hatch. They have met and overcome their hostility to the close proximity of each other by the first of the sexual displays – the sexual chase – and their ensuing behaviour is gradually working towards the production of eggs and young. After the establishment of the pair they search for nest sites and then build the nest. At intervals they break off to relax, preen and court each other. This may include courtship feeding in which the male brings food and gives it to the female, which, in addition to stimulating and strengthening the pair bond, is thought by some authorities to be helpful to the female at a time when the eggs are forming within her body. The male also becomes accustomed during this period to bringing food to the female so that when the eggs are laid he can feed her on the nest without hesitation. The male normally approaches the female with food in a rather upright posture, showing excitement by flicking his wings. The female in return crouches and stretches out her wings and quivers them. She is now rather below the male, and holds her beak skywards to receive the food. This is an attitude of solicitation which is common, with variations, to many bird species. The male then feeds her and she relaxes.

This is the high-intensity display but courtship feeding does not begin like this. In its low-intensity form, in Goldfinches, for instance, I watched a pair sitting side by side on a twig and at intervals in nest-building, they turned their heads and began 'kissing' each other, touching the tips of their bills. They did this for a minute or so at a time. No excitement was evinced and no food was passed. Later the pair separated and eventually went to their nest-building. A day or two later I found the female crouching slightly by the side of the male and once more they touched beaks as though feeding. There was only a little more excitement – still no food was passed. Courtship feeding began properly when food was passed. My point is that many of the displays that you may see in gardens and elsewhere develop from very small, less obvious beginnings.

The next stage in this sequence of events is copulation. In the case of the female Goldfinch she solicits with her legs bent, wings out of the coverts and quivering, head up, beak open, calling a high-pitched 'tee-tee-tee-tee'. The male approaches her excitedly as usual, but instead of feeding her he mounts her and they copulate. This is a rather general picture of the way that courtship displays lead up to copulation and there are a number of variations between species. Some experts think that courtship feeding, acts as a releaser for coition, and it occurs just prior in a number of species.

The act of copulation may be very beautiful, although perhaps for most passerines after the short preliminary display it is rather abrupt and may only take a few seconds. On the other hand, the Avocet goes through quite a long routine. A pair may be feeding vigorously in a shallow lagoon, sweeping their bills through the mud below the water. After a time they will stop feeding and, while standing in shallow water, begin preening, at first fairly normally, then exaggeratedly. Suddenly, the female will lower her head and neck until her chin is resting on the water and remain in this position, occasionally jerking her head a fraction from side to side, to solicit the male. He will continue preening even more vigorously and move towards her, finally, standing quite close. After a moment or two he will move behind and always touching her, will then move to the other side while still preening and splashing her with water. He will continue moving from one side to the other for three or four minutes, and then without any warning, will suddenly jump sideways onto the female's back and, with wings raised almost vertically, sink down on his tarsi and tuck his cloaca under her body, until they touch. Coition lasts only four or five seconds and after it is over the male slithers forward and sideways off the female and, almost always, the pair momentarily cross bills as they run apart for a few metres before they begin preening again in a more normal manner.

When the young start begging for food their soliciting postures are virtually the same as that used by the female. The Reverend E. A. Armstrong thinks that courtship feeding in adults is a recrudescence of the begging behaviour of the young.

Several species of birds have displays, in which the bills are touched, which lead to courtship feeding and copulation. The billing of the Puffin where a pair or up to six or so individuals may knock their bills together or where Gannets spar with their bills are examples of this.

Related to the solicitation posture are certain types of flight. Many land and water birds, use a 'moth' flight in which the bird flies comparatively short distances with wings quivering rapidly, but not very deeply. This

A typical Avocet aggression display involves 'edging', this entails the defending bird walking side by side with the intruder, apparently displaying its black-and-white pattern and occasionally fluttering its wings.

flight is often used, if not always, in circumstances which have some sexual connotation, for instance often just before, or just after, copulation. There are variations too on this flight: for instance, the Wheatear flies fast and erratically over his territory in what I call the 'zig-zag' flight.

The 'butterfly' flight or 'bat' flight, in which the wings beat deeply and more slowly, is more often used in territorial circumstances. The Greenfinch uses it regularly in spring. Besides finches it is used by the auks as they fly onto their cliffs. Hen Harriers and many other species have similar display flights.

It is of course almost impossible to give anything like a complete summary of the courtship displays of birds. Their diversity has been best surveyed by the Reverend E. A. Armstrong in his book, *The Ethology of Bird Displays and Behaviour*, which, although written some time ago, has been revised and is a wonderful compilation of the descriptions of displays and their interpretations. It covers not only the courtship displays but all bird displays. There is also a small paperback *Discovering Courtship Displays* by the same author.

Nesting behaviour

While a pair are going about the initial stages of territory formation and defence, as well as courtship display, they have also been preparing to nest. One of the important aspects of most territories is that they should provide adequate shelter for the construction of that specialized form of shelter, the nest which must be able to protect the eggs and young from both the rigours of the climate and predators. Almost any position that affords protection and support can hold a nest, from holes in the ground to flimsy branches at the tops of trees. Most nests that are built above ground are found in suitable forks in trees and bushes. The larger nests are found on the thicker branches while some nests, like the Redpoll's are found 12 metres up at the ends of branches, where they sway about violently in strong winds.

Some nests are open like those of the Woodpigeon and Turtle Dove, others are domed like those of the Magpie, Long-tailed Tit and Wren. Some birds nest on the ground or in holes. Puffins and Manx Shearwaters are even able to dig their own burrows in some loose types of soil. The Wheatear makes use of a variety of holes in the ground as well as in walls. Its preference, however, is for a burrow with a comparatively small entrance and an escape chamber behind the nest, into which the incubating female or mobile young can run if a predator comes down the burrow. Holes in trees are also regularly used, woodpeckers and Marsh Tits bore their own, but many other species including Starlings, tits and owls use old holes that have either rotted away or been excavated. Treecreepers quite often nest under bark which is peeling off. Kingfishers and Sand Martins excavate holes in sand banks close to water where they obtain their food supply. Along the sea-cliffs, especially where there are horizontal bedding planes, can be found colonies of seabirds. These bedding planes provide numerous ledges on which the auks and other species such as the Kittiwake nest. Because of the precariousness of the situation the young of these birds have developed special behaviour patterns to stop them from falling off.

Over the ages each species through the competition for suitable nest sites, has developed fairly specific types of nest so that an experienced person can identify a species simply by its nest and site.

The study of nests is fascinating, especially so after the eggs have been laid. However, one must remember that the nest holds very delicate objects. Searching for a nest may damage the eggs and young and could also sufficiently disturb the surrounding vegetation to induce the parents to

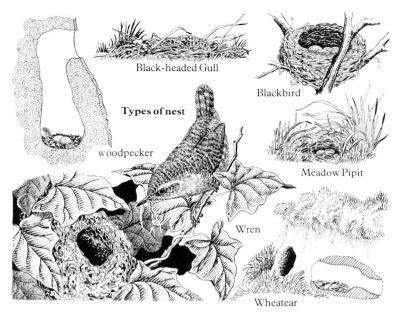

Types of nest

Black-headed Gull

Blackbird

woodpecker

Meadow Pipit

Wren

Wheatear

Eggs in ground nests tend to be cryptically coloured, giving them added protection. Eggs in hole nests tend to be brightly coloured which may help the adults to locate them.

desert or expose the nest to predators. Therefore searching for nests for its own sake should be discouraged. However, I am not suggesting the records should not be sought for the BTO nest record scheme. The BTO has its code of conduct for people taking part who realize that the scientific value of their investigation would be nullified by any disturbance of the birds.

Establishment of the nest site Often it is the female of the species which selects the nest site and my observations of Goldfinches and Wheatears have shown that the female will start to take material to two or three possible sites before finally deciding on the one that will be used. In the Blackbird again it is the female which usually decides on the nest site. In hole-nesting species, such as the Common Redstart, the male sometimes selects suitable nest-sites before the female arrives. Desmond Nethersole-Thompson describes in his book *The Greenshank* how both sexes of the Greenshank select nest sites. They walk over likely ground without actually forming any nest scrapes at first, then the male, sometimes with his mate, flies at intervals over his territory and from a height sings and displays with extraordinary passion and violence, after which he dives to the ground and either watches the female testing the ground for sites or occasionally leads her to others.

Some species, such as eagles, which spend the winter in their 'home range' may take several months deciding which site they are going to use. Others can make up their minds very quickly; when the RSPB bought the Lodge at Sandy some of the staff visited it one day rather late in April and put up several nest boxes. Two hours later they decided to look at the boxes before returning to London and found that a Blue Tit had already started to nest.

Some birds return to the same nest site in succeeding years particularly if they are on fairly permanent structures. Oystercatchers on Skokholm used to return to the same scrape on a rocky outcrop. Eagles, Buzzards and Kites return to the same tree or cliff ledge, while Swallows return to the same mud cup. Some of the returning birds would appear to be the same individuals that have used the site in previous years, but, on the other hand, some sites would appear to be 'traditional', in that they have been used by succeeding generations of birds. Indeed, the Loch Garten Osprey site has been used for nearly twenty years by a number of different individuals, although this would appear to be a special case as it is a protected site. Prior to 1954 the Osprey has been recorded by that fine chronicler of Scottish birds, Harvie Brown, as returning to sites which have been occupied on and off for many years. Birds of prey often have several choices of site which they might use in rotation.

A traditional nest site – one which is used on several occasions over a number of years by different pairs – presumably must have certain characteristics which suit the requirements of the species, making it an 'ideal' nest site or it may be that it is the only suitable site in the area. With larger birds, the choice of suitable nest sites is more limited and the building of a large nest takes some time and therefore it is advantageous for a pair to use an already established site. Evidence for the traditional use of nest sites in smaller birds is lacking, perhaps because the exact location of these small nests is difficult to describe. Wheatears on Skokholm tended to use burrows which had been used before by other pairs. W. B. Yapp tells of an ornithologist who visited some friends of his parents whom he had not visited for thirty years. He remarked that when he was a boy there always used to be a Goldcrest's nest in a particular cedar. He then got up and went to the tree and put his hand under the bough and flushed a Goldcrest off its nest. In a large tree which changes shape or form slowly there is time for some small bird nest sites to become traditional. It only remains for the observer to know and record the nest sites of an area well enough and long enough for them to be recognizable in the future.

Nests and nest building A nest may just be a cup-shaped depression scraped in the soil or a highly intricate structure woven together with a variety of different materials. An all-round naturalist that I know sometimes takes old birds' nests from a wood he knows well and identifies the plants and other materials of which the nests are composed. He can then trace how far the birds have travelled to collect the material for the nest.

Those birds which nest on rocky surfaces or in burrows use hardly any nesting material. Some ground-nesting birds may, by swivelling themselves around on their breast, make a scrape in the ground, to which they bring material. Some waders, such as Lapwings and Avocets, if they are close to their nest scrapes may pick up pieces and lay or toss them on the nest. Avocets seem to be able to build quite substantial nests in this way. Some material probably helps to camouflage the nest and eggs, such as when Stone-curlews and Oystercatchers line their nests with a few chips of rock or rabbit pellets.

Most song birds make use of what material there is to hand. A Wheatear I observed on Skokholm, began by taking in dried bracken or heather stems. The cavities of the rabbit nurseries which they were using were rather too large to hold the nest steady. The stems of these plants were the foundation into which they built a loose cradle of grasses which held the tighter-textured nest cup, also made with grasses. Finally the nest was lined with Rabbit and Soay Sheep hairs and the occasional Manx Shearwater feather.

My observations of Goldfinches have shown that as well as using grasses they also use Forget-me-nots and Sweet Alyssum, which they placed corolla outwards on the nest. This had the effect of camouflaging the nest amongst the leaves of fruit trees, limes and cherries. The significance of flower gathering is not yet fully understood. Goldfinches are also one of the birds that makes use of spiders' webs to bind the first pieces of nest material to the twigs of the tree.

Mud is a well-used building material. Blackbirds and Song Thrushes line their nests with it, while Nuthatches plaster the entrance of their nest holes with it to reduce the size. The Swallow and House Martin are well known for using mud pellets to make up the cup of their nests which are often found under the eaves of houses.

The actual construction of the nest is an instinctive action; birds of the same species build nests that conform closely to a given pattern without any instruction. However, there is some evidence that birds build better nests as they grow older and benefit from experience. The movements which they use to build the nest, therefore, tend to be rather stereotyped. There appears to be three movements which are common to most passerines. Professor R. A. Hinde calls them 'pulling and weaving', 'scrabbling' and 'turning'. In 'pulling and weaving', loose strands of nest material are pulled towards the breast of the bird, which is sitting in the cup of the nest, and then pushed down into the cup. The female 'scrabbles' by pressing down into the cup and pushing back hard with each leg alternately. In 'turning' the female turns round while sitting in the cup and thus shapes the cup of the nest. The female normally builds the nest, sometimes helped by the male. In a few species the male does the major part of the building assisted by the female. The notable exceptions, perhaps, are the unlined nests built by male Wrens and some other species which are used by the males for roosting. The time taken to build a nest may range from virtually a day or so to perhaps several months, or even years, in the case of a bird of prey which may add an odd stick to an already existing nest throughout the breeding season. Small passerines, which winter in Britain, may take as much as a month if bad weather intervenes and stops building. Summer visitors to this country, because they arrive later, build their nests rather more rapidly. Between two and three weeks elapsed between the first time that I saw a pair of Wheatears carrying nest material and the laying of the first egg. Generally speaking, the further north the species is nesting, the quicker the nest is built because the breeding season is shorter. In cases of necessity, when for instance a nest or clutch of eggs has been destroyed, repeat nesting and even second clutch nests can be built in a day or so. In Wheatears, I found the first eggs of repeat clutches – that is clutches replacing those destroyed – two days to four days after the first clutch had been destroyed.

Eggs and egg-laying Very few birds nest all the year round, most have a restricted breeding season, which in Britain and the temperate world is in spring and summer. Dr David Lack has shown that breeding is so timed that the young are usually raised when their food is most plentiful. Various external factors which differ with latitude and with the environment control the breeding season. In the higher latitudes of Europe the day length is the most dependable factor. Here Dr Lack has shown that the average clutch size of the Robin and other species is larger in the northern parts of its range than in the southern. This is so that they can take advantage of the longer hours of daylight during the short breeding season. In our temperature zone increasing warmth in spring is apparently one of the factors which brings the birds into breeding condition. An example of this is that resident species like the Song Thrush and Blackbird, breed earlier in mild early springs than in cold late ones.

Natural selection has, broadly speaking, eliminated those birds whose breeding season did not coincide with the most abundant food supply. Local conditions, however, may vary the length of the breeding season from year to year and may also affect the number of broods raised by each pair.

If you are studying the life history of a small population of birds within easy reach of your home, you can find out for yourself when the breeding season occurs and how much it varies by recording the dates on which eggs are laid and by recording fairly simple data on the weather. The Nest Record Scheme of the BTO will provide you with forms to which you can finally transfer your field data: the nest record cards themselves tell you what data you need to collect, not only to record the breeding season but also details of the nest site, habitat and so on. You need to collect quite a lot of records but they will also be of use to the BTO in building up a national picture of the breeding seasons.

One of the key dates in a bird's life is the laying of the first egg. Whereas in mammals the early stages of the development of the embryo take place in the mother's womb, it would be inconvenient and very dangerous for a bird to carry the additional weight of five or six young in her body. She would be greatly handicapped as she flew, at risk from predators and if, by some mischance, she was caught and killed, her offspring would die too. By disposing of her eggs into her nest, she remains agile. If the eggs are lost to some predator, she has a chance to escape and produce a repeat clutch.

The essential parts of an egg are the yolk, albumen and shell with a membraneous lining. Just before the eggs leave the oviduct the colour which is provided by two basic pigments – a blue or blue green and a brown olive – is deposited on the shell. Spots are produced by the pigment gland while the egg is stationary in the oviduct, but if the egg is moving streaks are produced. The function of the colouring is chiefly to camouflage the eggs and many which are laid in the open, such as those of the Little Tern and Ringed Plover which are generally stone or dun-coloured with spots, are extremely difficult to see. Many others, such as the Lapwing, Partridge, Skylark and Meadow Pipit, have a buff-brown basic colour. Birds of prey produce a series of warm red-brown eggs which, unfortunately, prove very attractive to egg collectors. Those eggs which are well hidden in holes or in deep nests and do not need camouflage are often pale or even white, and it is thought that these light-coloured eggs might help the parent find them more easily in the dark hole.

Incubation period There are no sharp divisions between one stage and the next. Even though many of a bird's actions have been building up to egg-laying, nest-building may continue after the first egg has been laid as may also some of the courtship displays, particularly copulation and courtship feeding. Normally small birds will lay one egg each day, often in the early morning, which is the time that it takes the eggs to form round the ripe ovum. Large birds may lay theirs every other day as the larger eggs take longer to form. Each species tends to lay a clutch size which has been adapted by natural selection to correspond with the largest number of young for which the parents can, on average, provide enough food. Dr David Lack has shown that clutches above the normal size are at a disadvantage because the young are weakened by under-nourishment and as a result fewer survive than from clutches of the normal size.

Some birds, normally those large birds with long incubation periods, characteristically lay one clutch a year. Others may lay two, three or infrequently more clutches, and probably all but a few species of birds will replace the first if it is destroyed shortly after it is laid.

The number of days needed to incubate the eggs may be as few as eleven in some of the warblers, but up to fifty-three days, in the case of a Fulmar incubating a single egg. Normally the species which have open nests incubate their eggs for the shortest period: Wrens and Long-tailed Tits, for instance, which have domed and soundly constructed nests, may have incubation periods lasting fourteen to eighteen days. Most birds incubate, or cover the eggs, for about 60% to 80% of the time it takes them to hatch but some species may remain on them for longer periods. For instance, the female Goldfinch, fed on the nest by the male, may incubate the eggs for as much as 96% of the time the eggs are in the nest. Birds like Manx Shearwaters and Fulmars, whose eggs need to be incubated for seven to eight weeks, may stay as long as five days on the nest before they go off for a similar period to feed and let their mates take over. Full incubation usually begins, in passerines, just before the last egg is laid, which helps to ensure that the eggs hatch at about the same time.

Normally, the female incubates the eggs and keeps them warm by shuffling them in order to touch the incubation patches on her belly. Most species of birds, prior to incubation, develop these feather-free patches of thickened skin on the ventral surface of the body, where a rich supply of blood vessels facilitates the transfer of body heat to the eggs. These patches generally develop about four to six days before the eggs are laid. They persist throughout the incubation period and into the early part of the brooding period when they begin to return to normal.

When males do share in incubating, they are generally amongst the less colourful, and in certain passerine species they lack incubation patches. They sit on the nest quite regularly, just keeping the eggs warm whilst their mates are away. In the exceptional cases of the Dotterel and the Red-necked Phalarope the males do all the incubating. The Gannet has no brood patch and places both webs of its feet over the egg, and the warmth of the web is responsible for incubation.

The male's duties in this early part of the nesting period are to defend the territory and the nest. At this point, the males, some of which have been silent since pair formation, start singing again. At times they give the appearance of considerable idleness. Now song has not only the effect of keeping intruders out but also, at least in the early stages of the incubation period, of giving the female confidence in her new situation.

Young and their development Technically, the young birds from the time they hatch until they can fly are called 'pulli'. But I shall call them 'nestlings' whilst they are in the nest, 'chicks' until they can fly and then 'juveniles' until they moult. During the incubation period the egg gradually becomes lighter and the shell weaker. A day or so before hatching the embryo develops two structures which help it to break out of the shell: firstly, a strong muscle at the back of the neck, and secondly, a blunt, horny, calcareous spike – the egg-tooth – on the tip of the upper bill; both disappear within a few days of hatching.

The first external evidence of hatching is a star-shaped crack that appears on the side of the egg near the larger end which is caused by the embryo's egg-tooth pressing against the inside of the egg-shell. The beak moves very slowly and very spasmodically around the inside of the egg and gradually the top is cut off. Just before it breaks out the embryo's first calls establish contact with its parents. Depending upon the species, and the weather, hatching may take from as little as an hour or two to two or three days; grebes hatch out within a few hours.

Once hatched, nestlings of different species show different degrees and methods of development: one group known as 'altricial' young are helpless when hatched. They are also called 'nidicolous' in that they remain in the nest for an extended period. They are entirely dependent on their parents for food and have a brightly-coloured gape surrounded by a soft and puffy

The Greenfinch builds a fragile nest about two and a half metres above the ground. They are often found in Hawthorn bushes which are popular nesting and feeding habitats for many small birds.

light-coloured edge which shows the adults where to put the food. They are usually naked at hatching or have only a sparse down on the dorsal regions which may possibly help to keep them warm and also hide them.

On the other hand, 'precocial' young are capable of walking or swimming soon after hatching. They may be dependent on their parents for food for a day or so or may immediately join the parents in searching for food. These young birds are also called 'nidifugous' in that they leave the nest almost immediately after hatching. They are covered with a dense down which is cryptically coloured, and, when the parent calls the alarm notes, they 'freeze' and become extremely difficult to see.

The majority of altricial species can fly at about seventeen days and become actually independent of their parents at about twenty-eight days. Some species of altricial nestlings leave the nest before they can fly and this departure from the nest is correlated with both the safety of the nest and the size of the bird. Nestlings hatched in a hole undergo a longer period of nest life than a chick hatched in an open nest and, as a general rule, the larger the species the longer it takes to develop. The Cuckoo is one notable exception; its young develop very rapidly because some development of the embryo may start while the egg is within the female. As a result the egg, which is laid later than its hosts', often hatches out first.

The weight of the nestlings of most passerines at hatching is approximately 66% of the weight of the fresh eggs, and about 6% to 8% of the weight of the adult female. However, it increases rapidly during nest life until at the time of leaving the nestlings weigh only 20% to 30% less than the female and in some species they are somewhat heavier than their parents.

The young of small perching birds pass through five stages of development. During the first three or four days the nestlings grow rapidly, their feather quills are visible beneth the skin and gradually force their way through. Their chief instinctive activities are stretching up their heads and neck and gaping when a parent brings food and, second, stretching out to defecate. They might also make their first food calls. In the second stage their eyes open and their weight increases rapidly. They begin to preen the opening feather quills, and the control of body temperature is established. At birth the nestlings are cold-blooded like reptiles. As soon as the female leaves the nest, their temperature drops towards air temperature. I studied the change in temperature control in nestling Wheatears. By inserting a small resistance thermometer among the young in the nest I was able to see how the difference in temperatures gradually decreased between the maximum, when the female was brooding, and the minimum recorded temperature after she had been away to feed. At the same time the percentage of time that the female spent brooding the young also decreased. When the nestlings were six-days old, and had a thin covering of feathers, the female no longer brooded them and their temperature remained constant.

In the third stage, more motor co-ordinations appear: the nestlings cower in fear; they can stretch their wings upwards and sideways; they can scratch their heads, shake themselves, fan their wings and flutter them when begging. A new series of call notes also appears. They are now capable of regulating their body temperature, and are well-feathered individuals. Some may be independent of the nest and their nest mates and be able to care for their feathers and move about to escape enemies. They can inform their parents of their whereabouts and respond to the parents' alarm notes. At this stage they will leave the nest if disturbed prematurely.

During the fourth stage, the nestlings that still remain leave the nest. At first, behaviour is characterized by silence, except when calling for food, and by general immobility. Their chief advance is the acquisition of flight. They also begin to show various independent feeding activities such as wiping the bill, pecking at objects, and picking up food.

The fifth and final stage of their development begins with the attainment of flight. They may still pursue the parents for food and this is the chief time when the young are conditioned by parental behaviour as to what they should fear and can be frequently heard calling in fear. They also develop antagonistic attitudes, such as threat postures and fighting. Finally they become independent of their parents.

The nearly-hatched precocial chicks, such as Lapwings, Moorhens and so on, by contrast with the development of nidicolous or altricial young birds, are rather well-proportioned except for the wings which are relatively small and undeveloped. The chicks are thickly covered with down feathers called neossoptiles on all the feather tracts. As in the altricial young the white egg-tooth is conspicuous but by contrast the rictal region is not enlarged and puffy and therefore not obvious to the parents. The chick shows quick response to visual and auditory stimuli, the eyes are open and both vision and hearing are already developed. The body temperature is partly established but the birds still need brooding for a few days.

Depending on the species, the weight of the precocial chick when it hatches ranges between 1% and 6% of that of the adult female. This decreases between hatching and the first feed but thereafter the young bird's weight increases steadily. The main feathers appear about five to six days after hatching on the scapular and the tail feather tracts. In aquatic species feathers are first evident on ventral feather tracts. The feathers on the wings and back appear between the first and the third weeks.

Most precocial chicks remain from about three to twenty-four hours in the nest after they have hatched, while they dry off. They rapidly become increasingly active, standing up and walking and running about. If they are waterbirds they may even swim. They peck at objects in the first stages of learning in order to discover what they can eat. When they rest they customarily sit on the tarsi with their heels touching the ground. Feeding begins on the first day out of the nest, and quite surprisingly, they search for, find and pick up food independently of their parents. They can already respond to the food-calls of parents and take food from the parents' bills or from the ground where the parents have placed it. Many aquatic chicks are more dependent and require assistance from parents in gathering food: young grebes, for instance, wait on the surface until their parents emerge with food. During the first three days after hatching the young birds begin to display virtually all the activities associated with the parents, except for breeding and flying. They sun themselves, swim, use feet for scratching themselves. They can call alarm notes, 'freeze' and peck at each other. Harmless fighting occurs and a definite social bond is evident. In many of these birds the brood persists as a unit until autumn or winter comes along.

What really has happened is that with precocial birds the first three stages of development of the altricial birds have already passed in the egg.

Parental care In the nidicolous species one of the first duties of parents is to dispose of the egg shells which could otherwise give away the position of the nest; they are either eaten or carried away as soon as they have been vacated by the nestlings. The nidifugous young vacate the empty eggs and the nest itself fairly rapidly so there is little point in moving the empty egg shells, though many do. In the nidicolous species brooding of

Wheatears nest in holes in the ground but will use a variety of artificial sites such as dry-stone walls, drain-pipes and even tins. The holes sometimes have an escape chamber behind the nest in case predators enter the burrow.

the nestlings appears to be a continuation of the incubation instinct and the parents share brooding in the same proportion as they shared incubation.

After the eggs have hatched the males sing less often and show less aggressiveness in the defence of the territory, although they become more aggressive towards predators and human beings as the time approaches for the young to leave the nest. Even though they take only a small part in incubation, the males share in the feeding of the young and obviously they then have less time to sing or to fight with territory competitors. In the first few days after hatching the female broods tight, particularly until the young gain temperature control. In open nests, even after brooding proper has finished, the females will shelter the young from the sun and rain, spreading their wings in order to do so.

Parents do not feed nidicolous young immediately after hatching. Normally they bring the first food after an interval of two or three hours: in some species the interval may be much longer. But once they start bringing food the parents work at an increasing rate until by the time the young are ready to leave the nest they are rushing from one food source to the next in a frenzied fashion. The young birds soon become aware of their parents' approach and they instinctively respond by a begging behaviour which initially involves the thrusting up of their necks with open mouths which show their bright-coloured gapes and tongue spots and which in their turn provide targets at which the parents can aim the food.

When the parents arrive at the nest the young respond with varying degrees of intensity. It is the young bird with the quickest and most effective response that gets the food until the swallowing response is inhibited by a full oesophagus. If the food is in small particles and is not swallowed quickly enough the parents may remove it and place is in another mouth. The rate of feeding increases daily because of the increasing needs of the fast-growing young.

In many instances it is the largest bird which gets the most food but there are ways of ensuring fairly equal sharing out of food amongst young birds. Wheatears nest at the end of a long burrow and consequently there is only one direction from which food can be brought. Once the eyes of the nestling are open and they have learnt where the food comes from the hungriest chick tends to sit at the edge of the nest nearest the entrance. As it is closest to the adult it is fed in each successive visit until it is so full that it has to defecate. It then clambers up on to the rim of the nest, and turns its cloaca outwards. Whilst it is up, and the parent is removing the faecal sac, the next hungriest young bird shuffles into its place. The bird on the rim, his task completed, has to struggle over the others to the back of the nest and sit there until it has digested what it has eaten and begins to feel hungry enough to struggle for the chief and favourite positions. Thus a rotation in the order of feeding is ensured.

In birds of prey the incubation of their two or three eggs which are laid two days apart usually begins with the first egg laid and consequently, if three eggs are laid, the first-hatched gets a lot more food than the last-hatched bird. Once started, this disparity in size is maintained throughout the period that the youngsters are in the nest. Thus, if there is an abundance of food the female eagle may be able to rear all three nestlings, but if there is a shortage then perhaps only the first-hatched will survive, having eaten its nest siblings.

Nest sanitation is important in order to prevent disease, and to lessen the chance of the nest being discovered. In nidicolous young, defecation usually occurs immediately after feeding although it may not occur after every food particle is brought. Generally speaking, the faecal sac, depending on age, is a mass of semi-solid uric acid and darkish intestinal excreta enveloped in thick mucus which is easily portable by parents. These sacs are regularly disposed of by the parents either throughout the nest life or, in some species, only in the first part of the nestling period. When the nestlings of some species are very small the parents will eat the excreta.

There is no necessity for nidifugous species to produce faecal sacs. Seabirds void their excrement over the edge of a cliff ledge and other nidifugous birds are constantly on the move and there is little chance of an accumulation of faeces.

Break-up of the family The time when the young leave the nest and become independent of their parents is the period when they are in greatest danger. For almost all species, the mortality rate between leaving the nest and sexual maturity is very high. Three-quarters of the young birds of prey, for instance, die before they reach sexual maturity.

While in the nest, the nestling will have been well protected from its enemies and the elements, and food will have been brought to it regularly. When the bird leaves the nest it will already be equipped, however, with a moderate range of instinctive reactions.

Some young birds which nest on the ground, are able to walk or stagger some distance away. Birds which have been reared in nests in trees or on cliffs flutter down, while others fall down hard and are still able to survive. Young auks, in particular, seem to be well padded with a layer of fat so that, if, in their glide and flutter down from ledges to the sea, there is an error and they hit the rocks below, they often seem to bounce off alive with no broken bones. Swifts can fly from the moment they leave the nest and are, from that moment, independent. They have, however, stayed in the nest for a fairly long incubation period of five to eight weeks. Other seabirds, especially petrels and shearwaters are deserted by their parents some days before the young leave the nest burrow so that they too have to hunt for food by instinct alone.

For the most part the young when they leave the nest do not travel far at first. But they disperse ever more widely, learning to find their own food until, finally, they become independent of their parents. There used to be an idea that parent birds drove their young away. So far as I am aware there are no recorded instances of this happening, but I have seen an adult Wheatear which was producing a second brood, threaten one of its first brood young when the latter started to solicit for food two or three weeks after it had left the nest.

With Blackbirds it would seem that there is some attachment between the family and that this may persist for some weeks after the young have left the nest. Young Yellow Wagtails may keep together until the onset of the moult. Robins leave the nest when they are fourteen-days old and finally become independent when they are about five-weeks old – although the female may well have deserted them when they are about three-weeks old in order to raise another brood.

Some wader families, like that of the Greenshank, for instance, which do not have second broods, travel together from one area to another in search of food until the young become proficient in hunting and can look after themselves. The bigger birds of prey often remain in the area of the 'home range' for several weeks before they disperse.

It is rather difficult to find out how the individual young birds actually fare at this time of the year. They are no longer restricted to a territory although some species may defend an area in which they may be feeding for some days. Even if the young are colour-ringed, they can move so far that you can quickly lose touch with an individual and, perhaps, the only thing you can do is watch and record what you see of the odd bird and gradually piece together a general picture of their behaviour.

Geographical distribution

Amateurs have probably contributed as much to the knowledge of the geographical distribution of birds throughout the world as to any branch of ornithology. While the British Empire was still spread around the globe, the colonial servants, soldiers and sailors, as well as a number of travellers and explorers who probed the various corners of the Earth, were curious observers and keen recorders. The problem of identifying species and their geographical forms was very different to what it is today. There were few comprehensive handbooks at the turn of the century or even thirty years ago. When I became warden of Skokholm in 1947 there were no field guides, and to identify European birds not recorded in Witherby's *Handbook of British Birds* we use Bree's *Birds of Europe* in four volumes which was very old-fashioned. The early ornithologists in their travels round the world had to use the gun. They collected large numbers of specimens which they labelled and brought back home to form the present museum collections. With the help of these museums they gradually built up the picture of what particular populations and groups of birds formed species, and how they were distributed throughout the world. Some people may be rather horrified to think that birds might have been shot for scientific reasons but we must remember that taxonomy owes nearly everything to the museums and private collections of birds. Also without these collections we might not have the coloured plates of birds that are found in the handbooks and field guides today. There is, thankfully, very little need for collecting today in Britain and Europe and because of the original work and the collections of others we have books of such excellence that as amateurs we can pursue some of the aspects of the study of geographical distribution without having to resort to killing.

The study of the geographical distribution of birds includes firstly, the study of the complete world range of a species and its populations as they are today, as distinct from the study of its local distribution which may only depend on the availability of suitable habitats. Secondly, it includes the study of the way in which species have originated and how their distributions have changed.

One of the remarkable facts about the distribution of birds is that although they are able to fly long distances, their range is generally limited to specific areas of the world. A few species are fairly cosmopolitan: the Osprey, for instance, which now breeds in a number of places in Scotland and news of which hits the headlines almost every year, breeds in Europe,

Asia, Australia, and North America and winters in South America and Africa. The House Sparrow is another which, chiefly because of man's helping hand, has a world-wide range. The Barn Owl, now comparatively rare in this country, ranges widely over other parts of the world. At the other extreme, some species may be limited to one small island: for instance, a warbler on Aldabra in the middle of the Indian Ocean is entirely specific to that island. The Galapagos Archipelago, which comprises a number of small isolated volcanic islands in the Pacific Ocean, has several species which are restricted to one or more of them.

The distribution of a species includes both its breeding and non-breeding ranges which may be markedly different: Swallows and warblers breed in the northern hemisphere but winter in South Africa; Arctic Terns breed in the far north and winter well south of the Equator. In other species there may be a slight overlap in ranges: the breeding and non-breeding ranges of Robins overlap. Other species have a vertical element in their range – Snow Buntings nest on high ground in high latitudes but winter along coastal regions. Dippers tend to move downstream from the higher levels of the hills in winter.

If you examine details of the distribution of different groups of birds, various factors will begin to emerge; in particular you will notice that certain regions are characterized by the presence of species peculiar to them. The earlier ornithologists found that attempts to describe the avifaunas of the different regions in terms of traditional continents were not particularly satisfactory. For instance, they found that the Sahara Desert rather than the Mediterranean Sea constitutes a latitudinal barrier to the dispersal of birds in Europe. Similarly Europe and Northern Asia seem to form a single faunal region. The idea of these faunal region was originally suggested for birds by P.L. Sclater in 1858 and was modified later for animals in general by A.R. Wallace (see map opposite).

The Palaearctic region in which we live is one of the largest zoogeographical regions yet it is relatively poor in bird species with only sixty-nine families. It has only one unique family – the Prunellidae, the family to which the Dunnock belongs – but it shares forty-eight families with the Nearctic of North America. The richest area for bird life is the Neotropical region of South America with eighty-six families and over 1,500 species.

Quite recently the idea of 'continental drift' has been generally accepted by the scientific world and it is now thought that the continents as we see them today were once part of a 'super-continent' which have since drifted apart. This theory would explain certain peculiarities in the distribution of plants and animals. For instance, you might find that a certain group of animals have more affinity with a group on another continent than with the others on their own continent.

During the course of the evolution of birds, conditions on Earth have changed considerably, often from one extreme to another. Droughts, ice-ages, earthquakes and floods have all had their effect upon the face of the

Zoogeographical regions of the world

Conventional geography does not lend itself to the study of animal distribution and the concept of faunal regions shown opposite do roughly correspond with some facts of avian distribution.

The drifting continents

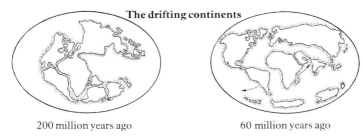

200 million years ago   60 million years ago

After many years of argument the principle of continental drift seems to be accepted by scientists and now offers a satisfactory explanation for the distribution of certain animals and plants which hitherto had puzzled scientists.

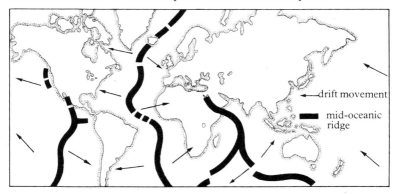

drift movement

mid-oceanic ridge

globe. Therefore birds must be able to adapt to their environment if they are to survive and as the environment changes they must be able to evolve to take account of the change, or they must be able to move elsewhere. The geographical distribution of birds is therefore the result of the gradually changing landscape and an evolving bird population. Birds have an inherited tendency to disperse from their place of birth and invade new areas. They are usually very mobile, though their power of flight can vary considerably. Crossbills and Nutcrackers manifest a form of dispersal following seasons of abundant food and a marked growth in population as a result of which large numbers erupt across the barriers of their normal range. Population pressure promotes range expansion in other species and it is often the young which travel furthest. Physical boundaries such as seas and mountains act as a buffer to these spreads. These barriers can sometimes be overcome; for example, various landbirds crossed the Pacific Ocean in large enough numbers to establish breeding populations in the Galapagos Archipelago.

Probably the decisive factors in determining the range of a bird are the climate and the nature of the soil – these two factors determine the vegetation and consequently the food, cover, nest sites and other important elements. The change in climate together with the changes in the habitat have probably been the cause of the decline in Britain and elsewhere of the range of the Red-backed Shrike and the Wryneck. The Cetti's Warbler which has recently invaded England from the continent will, however, probably be confined by the climate from spreading from the south of England. Another factor which can prevent the spread of a species is the presence of another species which has similar ecological requirements and will therefore compete with the new arrival.

The study of the ranges of birds is still a study in which a great army of amateurs participate, or can participate providing they submit accurate records to their county bird recorders. Many birdwatchers are interested in the unusual bird which turns up outside its range. Sometimes the appearance is an accident in that a migratory American bird might have been wind-drifted across the Atlantic or a bird migrating northwards to Scandinavia might have been drifted under overcast skies across the North Sea to the shores of Britain. On the other hand, the appearance of some rare species may be the forerunner of an invasion. The Collared Dove, for example, has become 'dynamic' in the last fifty to a hundred years and has swept across Europe from Turkey. It was first recorded in Britain in the early 1950s and has now, in a matter of twenty or thirty years, virtually colonized the whole of Britain. It has increased to such an extent that it is now considered by some to be a pest, and it probably holds some sort of a record for a quick change from inclusion in lists of birds especially protected into lists of pest species.

There are various other species whose range is gradually changing. The Serin, which is closely allied to the domesticated Canary, is another species which swept across Europe and is now on the other side of the Channel,

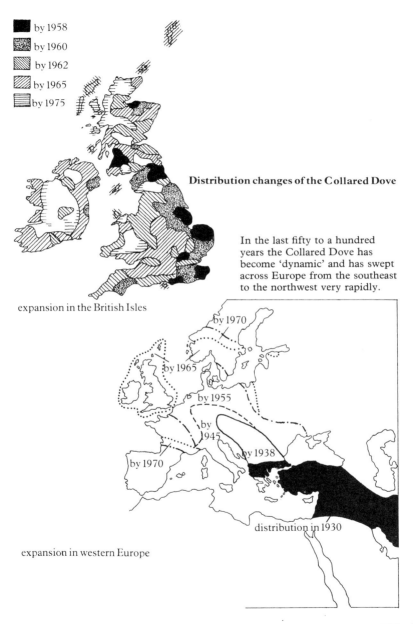

by 1958
by 1960
by 1962
by 1965
by 1975

Distribution changes of the Collared Dove

expansion in the British Isles

In the last fifty to a hundred years the Collared Dove has become 'dynamic' and has swept across Europe from the southeast to the northwest very rapidly.

by 1970
by 1965
by 1955
by 1945
by 1938
by 1970

distribution in 1930

expansion in western Europe

and, although the occasional individual has been recorded on this side, they have not yet really established a bridgehead in Britain. Several species have re-established themselves in Britain in recent years, sometimes because their habitat has re-appeared. The Avocet, Black-tailed Godwit and Black Tern used to nest in the Fens of England over a hundred years ago until drainage destroyed their habitats. Changes in land use in recent years have once more produced the sort of terrain – rather wet – on which these birds can complete their nesting cycles, and the RSPB has acted to purchase and manage this land to ensure that this time they remain with us. Oddly enough, fewer species are 'retreating' from Britain at present than are colonizing.

The decline in the distribution of the Stone-curlew and the Wheatear in Britain is probably related to the activities of man. Their habitat is ideally of a steppe or semi-desert nature, which, in Britain, is only found naturally on the summit plateaux of high mountains. The presence of these two species in lowland Britain was mainly the result of the felling of forests and the introduction of sheep and rabbits to the land. The spread of myxomatosis and the decline in sheep numbers has meant that the heavily grazed habitat suitable for the two species has decreased. What propelled these species into Britain is not known, but I think that suitable lowland habitats for the Wheatears probably only appeared in the twelfth century.

The lists of birds that some of us keep when we go out in the field no matter where we are, can either be a waste of paper or can provide a record of value. If you put nothing but a tick against a bird's name you are at least making some record. On the other hand, the more accurately you record your observations the more valuable they will be. The figures you record can become a base line against which you can compare figures you obtain from later counts in the same habitat. Records like these are often the basis of county bird reports which in turn have been used for more extensive reports, for example, John Parslow's *Breeding Birds of Britain and Ireland* and the British Ornithologists' Union's *The Status of Birds in Britain and Ireland*. Therefore it is worth trying to add as much information as possible to your field lists.

Ocean transects are a valuable way of learning about the distribution of birds at sea, but sadly most people now travel by air. However, for those who do travel by sea the Royal Naval Birdwatching Society has special report forms which help to add a basis of uniformity to the records. Indeed, anyone who is lucky enough to be going on a long ocean voyage should get in touch with the RNBWS first and find out how he or she can contribute to this area of study.

Ecology and habitat

Ever since I read Charles Elton's classic book, *Animal Ecology* published by Sidgwick and Jackson, which was first published in 1927 and is still in print, I have been fascinated by the subject of ecology. Elton originally described ecology as 'scientific natural history' and this is still a valid description. Another definition of ecology is the 'study of animals and plants in relation to their environment'. Professor Eugene Odum, a well-known American ecologist, states that it is more in keeping with modern emphasis to define ecology as the study of the structure and function of habitats or the places where birds and other animals, as well as plants, live. He and other scientists like him, are particularly interested in the transfer of energy through the ecosystem (the community of living and non-living material in an environment), and how this energy, contained in the food or nutrients moves through the different levels. Basically, the cycle begins with the chemicals from the non-living material, such as rocks, being absorbed by the plants. These are eaten in their turn by animals, which may be eaten by other animals and which finally return to the soil in one form or another. This process is usually assisted by organisms which break down the dead protoplasm.

This type of study generally speaking is beyond the ability of the average birdwatcher with limited time at his disposal. However, we do have wonderful opportunities to observe birds in relation to their environment and observe how these needs are met by the various components of their habitat.

Even within its normal geographical range a bird does not have a completely continuous distribution and this may be affected by several physical factors, such as temperature, light, the presence or absence of water, and the shape of the terrain. These in turn affect the vegetation and animal life and their inter-actions. The impact of all these factors shapes a bird's 'niche' which is defined as a bird's role within an ecosystem and its living place in the habitat. For example, in the context of its 'niche' the Wheatear could be broadly described as an insectivorous bird, which lives on open ground, including heavily grazed grassland and mountain plateaux and avoids any form of thick cover, though it nests in holes or burrows. While, by contrast the Robin could be described as a mainly insectivorous bird which lives in rather dense woodland and woodland edges, rarely staying long from cover, and nests in holes.

Apparently a bird recognizes its habitat instinctively. On Skokholm the

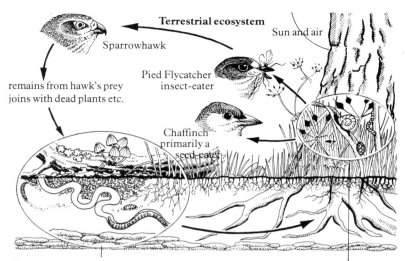

Terrestrial ecosystem

Sparrowhawk

Sun and air

remains from hawk's prey
joins with dead plants etc.

Pied Flycatcher
insect-eater

Chaffinch
primarily a
seed-eater

Decaying wood, leaf and plants are eaten by small
micro-organisms (detritus feeders). These with help
from worms, centipedes, etc., help replace the
goodness in the soil which the plants need to grow.

producers—plants, trees, etc.
primary consumers—snails,
beetles, flies, caterpillars, etc.

The terrestial ecosystem is basically a producer to consumer arrangement where
each level produces living material which is not only food for another level but
which, like trees, may affect the environment and provide habitat.

most heavily grazed grassland in the centre of the island attracted
Wheatears during the autumn passage, while on the spring migration they
tended to settle on the outer edges of the island where the soft peaty soil was
riddled with thousands of holes excavated by rabbits and seabirds, and
which was representative of the Wheatear's preferred nesting area. Thus
apparently their 'image' of their habitat differed according to the time of
year.

A number of systems of classifying habitats have been described over the
years, but none of them has been completely satisfactory perhaps, because,
as Charles Elton points out, no single kind of animal is entirely confined to
one component type of habitat. Another source of confusion is the tendency
of ornithologists to use botanical terminology to describe a habitat. This, to
my mind, is not entirely satisfactory as birds tend to be more affected by
such factors as the age or the density or the size of trees in a wood, as much
as by the species.

The system of nomenclature for habitats which is most generally used
today is based on a system originally devised by Charles Elton in his book
The Pattern of Animal Communities published by Methuen, which is one of
the best natural history books ever written and not read by nearly enough

amateur naturalists. In approaching the problem of describing habitats, he says: 'Any ecological classification of habitats needs to fulfil three requirements. The first is to divide up the landscape and its species network into different components that can be defined by discontinuities in the field; the second is that components of one kind should be recognizably similar though they can never be exactly so; and the third is that they should have some ecological meaning, that is contain groups that form communities in some real sense of the term.'

The BTO has produced a habitat classification for its 'Register of Ornithological Sites' and for other surveys. It is on two levels of hierarchy and can be used to describe in general terms the breeding habitats of most birds.

A		B
0 Woodland and scrub	0	Broad-leaved woodland (other than coppice)
	1	Coppice
	2	Even-aged coniferous plantation
	3	Uneven-aged coniferous plantation
	4	Mixed woodland
	5	Pioneer scrub
	6	Carr (fen woodland)
1 'Field' vegetation	0	Bracken
	1	Chalk downland and similar grasslands
	2	Machair (natural grassland on calcareous sand)
	3	Lowland dry heath
	4	Upland heather moor
	5	Upland grasslands
2 Wetlands (vegetation associated with fresh water)	0	Bog
	1	Wet heath or heath bog
	2	Fen and marsh
	3	Watercress beds (used and disused)
	4	Reedbed
	5	Turlough (grassy hollow on limestone)
	6	Watermeadow and wash
3 Water bodies (fresh)	0	Lowland river or stream
	1	Upland river or stream
	2	Ditch (artificial, less than 5 metres wide)
	3	Canal (artificial, more than 5 metres wide)
	4	Pond (less than 0·5 hectares)

3 Water bodies (fresh)
(continued)

5 Pool or tarn (0·5 to 5 hectares)
6 Lake or reservoir (more than 5 hectares)
7 Other water body, e.g. gravel pit or flash (less than 0·5 hectares)
8 Other water body (0·5 to 5 hectares)
9 Other water body (more than 5 hectares)

4 Open habitats (not coastal)

0 Exposed 'mud'
1 Exposed quarry face (sand, chalk, etc.)
2 High montane
3 Cliff and crag

5 Coastal

0 Mud
1 Saltmarsh
2 Coastal grazing marsh
3 Brackish pools and lagoons
4 Gravel and pebbles (beach, bar, spit, etc.)
5 Sand (flats or beach)
6 Sand dunes
7 Dune slack
8 Cliff
9 Stack or rocky island

6 Miscellaneous

0 Farmland, predominantly arable
1 Farmland, predominantly grazing
2 Farmland mixed
3 Hedgerows with mature trees
4 Hedgerows without mature trees
5 Disused railway track
6 Grassy areas with scattered trees (parkland, golf courses, etc.)
7 Sewage farms or purification works
8 Building and constructions
9 Waste land

This system is fine for describing general habitats but when dealing with differences between the habitats of some closely related species such as the Garden Warbler and the Blackcap you will run into difficulties, and will have to work out your own methods. Concentration on every little detail is often required to discover what limits a bird to a particular habitat.

Charles Elton in his book *The Pattern of Animal Communities*, having described the main habitat systems, goes on to point out that the terrestrial systems can be grouped into a series of habitats corresponding to an ecological succession from bare ground up to a climax woodland. He uses

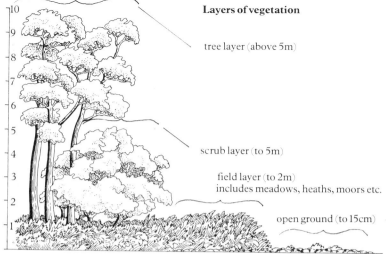

Layers of vegetation

tree layer (above 5m)

scrub layer (to 5m)

field layer (to 2m)
includes meadows, heaths, moors etc.

open ground (to 15cm)

metres

From a structural viewpoint terrestial habitats fall into a series of layers corresponding to a succession from bare ground to climax woodland. Their precise composition depends on a number of other factors such as soil type and climate.

four commonly recognizable formation types. *Open ground* includes the soil and any plants up to 15 centimetres in height. The *field layer* comprises meadows, heather moors, low bramble, and any stage towards the climax vegetation which is less than 2 metres high. *Scrub layer* grows to 5 metres high and any vegetation above that is the *woodland* or *tree layer* type. Although one is dealing here with different types of communities, the same stratification is quite often detectable in a climax or well-developed woodland, as A. J. Willis points out in his useful book, *Introduction to Plant Ecology*. Obviously the divisions of the strata are not precise as the birds do not keep to the special layers and it is often more valuable to study the actual perches or heights above ground at which the birds are feeding, nesting and so on.

Many people have made studies of the use that birds make of different levels of their habitat. They are often particularly interested in the 'niche' which the birds fill and whether there is competition, which may occur when two different species occupy the same habitat and seek similar food supplies. It is unlikely that both species will be equally competent and the less efficient will be at a disadvantage, especially when food is in short supply.

Dr Perrins, in his book, *Birds*, summarizes the differences in the feeding habits of some closely related members of the tit family. Dr Perrins and members of the Edward Grey Institute at Oxford found that in general

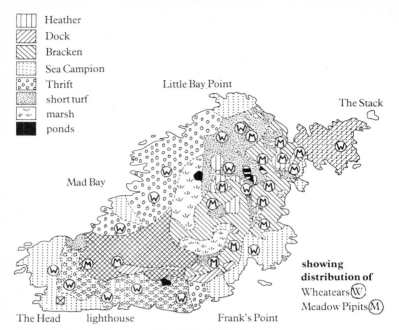

▭	Heather
▨	Dock
▧	Bracken
⬚	Sea Campion
⬚	Thrift
⬚	short turf
⬚	marsh
■	ponds

Little Bay Point

The Stack

Mad Bay

showing distribution of
Wheatears (W)
Meadow Pipits (M)

The Head   lighthouse   Frank's Point

Simplified vegetation map of Skokholm Island

This simple vegetation map of Skokholm shows how the Wheatear is found where the vegetation is short while the Meadow Pipit prefers taller vegetation. (After Jean Lawman).

terms Great Tits tended to feed low on Hazels or on the ground; Marsh Tits hunted low down on the large branches of Oak and Beech trees; Blue Tits, on the other hand, tended to feed high on Oak leaves and smaller twigs, while Coal Tits fed high up in conifers.

This type of study is worth repeating in different kinds of woods and in different parts of the country. It is hard and sometimes tedious work. However, although you may not learn anything new, you will gain an insight into the more detailed feeding arrangements of the species.

I have, personally, looked at the ways birds forage on the sandy shores and rocky coasts of the island of Alderney. I began this study originally while holidaying with my children and have continued it for several years. I wanted to establish how the different feeding techniques and hunting methods used by such waders as the Dunlin and Ringed Plover lessened the chances of the two species competing. Some of the animal life on which these waders feed is found on the surface, whilst others are found under rocks and seaweed or below the surface of the sand. In order to exploit this

The Dipper is a thrush which obtains its food from the bottoms of mountain streams. By spreading its wings it is able to use the flow of the water to overcome its natural buoyancy.

range of food the waders have different shapes and lengths of bill as well as different methods of feeding. Some waders stab at the surface of the mud, others like the Curlews and godwits wander about probing deeply. Plovers usually run for 50 to 100 centimetres and then search for food. Turnstones, as their name implies, turn over stones and seaweeds in their search for sandhoppers. Dunlins, in wet sand or mud, probe deeply but on hard and dry sand they can only peck at the surface.

Some extensive studies of all the factors which influence a bird in its choice of habitat have been made, chiefly by American ornithologists, but even so the distribution of a species through its habitat is still a relatively unexplored field in avian ecology. If you visit, for example, a number of different types of oakwoods with different types of coppicing and count the birds on each visit you may eventually deduce that a certain species shows a preference for a wood with certain characteristics. But you are unlikely to understand the reasons unless you study the bird itself and discover what use it is making of each part of the habitat.

As an example let us look at the use that the Wheatear makes of its habitat. As soon as the Wheatear arrives from the south it must feed, so that immediately it will discover whether food, which is neither too large nor too hard to eat, is available. The Wheatear hunts by hopping for a metre or two, or making a type of 'running hop' like so many of the chats and thrushes.

This gait requires that the ground must be fairly bare of vegetation or heavily grazed, otherwise the longer grasses and other plants would obstruct the bird's passage. Indeed, when the Wheatear does occasionally hunt amongst the longer grasses it often hovers like a Whinchat or Stonechat, before it drops in to the grass after its prey. Species which feed in the longer grasses, such as the Skylark and Meadow Pipit, tend to walk. Furthermore, they have a long hind-claw which can presumably act like a snowshoe, trapping a mass of grass-blades beneath it.

Almost every part of the habitat can be used for nest-sites. No birds nest underwater, unless you claim that the Dipper qualifies as it can use a ledge behind a waterfall. Several species do build floating nests, such as the Black Tern and Great Crested Grebe. Waders with precocial young nest in damp wetland habitats on which the young can forage for food within a day or two of hatching. On drier soil in suitable coastal areas hole-nesting birds such as the Puffin will be found. There is a similar variety of nesting preferences in woodlands: Chiffchaffs and Willow Warblers build on or close to the ground, while Garden Warblers and Blackcaps nest in the field layer. Linnets choose the thick cover of bushes and hedges. Higher up, Carrion Crows nest among the thicker branches, while Goldfinches and Redpolls squeeze their nests into the ends of branches. The holes and crevices are used by Robins, tits and woodpeckers. One of the most comprehensive surveys of the nest sites of British birds is to be found in a *Field Guide to Birds' Nests* by Bruce Campbell and James Ferguson-Lees.

While most species build their nests in cover, there are others which appear to prefer to see over long distances such as the Stone-curlew, and moorland species such as the Golden Plover. They nest in fairly open positions but their plumage disguises them or their eggs are cryptically coloured. Most birds of prey nest where they have good views over the surrounding countryside. It is interesting to ponder how small a field a Lapwing will nest in or how close to a hedge. Some species, particularly the small woodland birds, tend to use cover to hide from enemies. Cover can also be useful to the hunter. The Sparrowhawk's method of catching his prey, springs to mind, as it flies low over or round bushes, thus surprising his victim.

Almost whenever there is a bird you can study its living conditions. One of the great advantages of the study of birds in relation to their environment is that you have to be aware of the other animals and plants that make up the ecosystem, thus widening your interest into the functions and structures of nature.

Population Another aspect of ecology is the study of factors which promote or limit the growth of populations. Sometimes fluctuations occur when, for various reasons, populations may increase rapidly and then a hard spell of weather may reduce the numbers appreciably.

Sometimes fluctuations do occur when, for various reasons, populations may increase rapidly and then a hard spell of weather may reduce the numbers appreciably.

The fluctuations in the English populations of the Grey Heron have been studied since 1928, initially by Max Nicholson and local naturalists and more recently by members of the British Trust for Ornithology. Virtually every major slump in the Heron population has been linked with an excessively hard winter in which snow and ice have covered the pools and ditches in which they fish. After these slumps numbers increased again rapidly and then tended to flatten out at the previous level, where the size of the Heron population matches the availability of the natural resources. The census of the Grey Heron is one of the longest studies of a population ever made and what has already been discovered indicates its value. The study of any population or community of birds over many years in almost any habitat, would be of great value.

The numbers of some birds of prey and game birds, especially in the Far North, rise and fall in fairly regular cycles which are often linked with the cycles of abundance of the prey species. The Lemming, which is a small rodent, and which is preyed on by the Rough-legged Buzzard amongst others, becomes very abundant every three or four years. When the Lemming numbers crash the numbers of their associated predators crash too, which is when Rough-legged Buzzards may invade Britain in relatively large numbers. Incidentally this illustration emphasizes the point that it is the numbers of the prey that controls the numbers of the predators and not that the predator controls the numbers of its prey.

It used to be thought that numbers remained stable because the reproductive rate of the species was adjusted to its mortality rate. But Dr David Lack has shown in his book, *Natural Regulation of Animal Numbers*, that the reproductive rate of birds is probably the highest of which they are capable under the conditions in which they live. This means that a pair raises as many young as can be fitted into the time of the year when food is sufficiently abundant for raising young and that they lay on average the number of eggs which will give rise to the number of young that they can feed.

Many species of birds are able to adapt their clutch size to a particular condition. For instance, they may lay larger clutches at certain times of the year or larger clutches in some habitats than in others, or in some years than in others. The largest clutch size in the Wheatear tends to be laid in the first week in May which is normally the week when the largest number of clutches are laid. This is presumably because birds which laid at other times have been culled by natural selection because their offspring failed to survive. Similarly, Wheatears on the island of Skokholm, which is covered in grass, laid on average more eggs than a population of Wheatears on the stony shingle of Dungeness. The reason for this was probably that the Wheatear population of Dungeness had been artificially increased by the RSPB warden, Herbert Axell, who had placed nestboxes on the shingle especially for them. However, on the shingle there was very little grass available on the roots of which the moth caterpillar, one of the main items of young Wheatears, could actually feed.

Whilst birds raise as many broods as can be fitted into the period when food is sufficiently abundant for raising young, what they actually achieve depends on the age that they become sexually mature and how long they survive. Some birds become sexually mature in the year after they hatch, but gulls may take three years and eagles up to six years to reach maturity.

Small passerines that we see in our gardens tend to have an expectation of life of only about a year from the time that they are a month old. It is easy to assume that the Robin that you see and know so well is the bird you have known for years, whereas you may well have had a different one every year. In the chapter on ringing I have given a list of the maximum ages of some species as recorded by the BTO ringing scheme.

Birds die in a number of different ways, and jointly these factors, particularly those which are density dependent, counteract the fecundity of the species so that within the small fluctuations that occur the bird population remains relatively stable. Density dependent factors become more effective as the density of the population itself increases. The most likely causes of density dependent mortality are predation, lack of food and disease. An example of a density independent factor would be the mortality of young birds in the nest because of very heavy rain.

Predation, which is the killing of an individual of one species by the individual of another, may well be the most important mortality factor. Birds of prey and owls are most often thought of as predators but Magpies and crows may also be predators on other birds, especially during the nesting season. Foxes, rats, stoats, weasels, cats and man also join the band of creatures which are generally flesh-eaters and which feed on birds. Whilst predation may be rather final for the victim, it may well help the species as a whole, for generally weaker individuals tend to be killed.

Nests with eggs or nestlings particularly of those species which nest on the ground are very vulnerable. Even more hazardous are the lives of young birds a month or so after thay have left the nest and for many small passerines this is the period of heaviest mortality.

Although this mortality is not entirely due to predation. A shortage of food in the breeding season may well affect the number of young reared. A classic example is provided by the way some birds of prey stagger their laying in order that the eldest and strongest chick can survive in times when food is scarce. Occasionally when food is really short some birds of prey may not even nest.

Parasites can be another density dependent factor. The chief ectoparasites (those which live on the outer parts of the host's body) are biting lice, fleas, blue bottles, flat flies, louse flies, ticks and mites, many of which overwinter as eggs or larvae in nests. Some lice and mites eat at the feathers, the remainder suck blood and if they are present in a nest or on the bodies of the nestlings in very large numbers they can kill or seriously weaken the nestlings. Furthermore, some of them transmit diseases. One feather mite regularly denudes the head or neck of Blackbirds in late summer. Whilst it could be said that probably more than 80% of the birds in the world have one or more types of ectoparasite, a large number also carry internally some microscopic organisms in the blood, such as protozoa, fungi, bacteria and viruses, known collectively as endoparasites. One of the commonest protozoan diseases is probably avian malaria, and it has been estimated that 97% of wild birds may be infected with it.

Another common endoparasite is the mould *Aspergillus* which attacks the windpipes, lungs and air sacks of birds, particularly ducks and causes heavy losses especially during wet weather. The contagious disease 'foot pox' causes wart-like growths of the feet and the base of the bill of the House Sparrow which may result in the loss of toes or feet.

Where birds feed regularly at bird tables they may become infected with *Salmonella* organisms which are transmitted through bird droppings. They can cause widespread deaths and it is important to see that your bird table is properly sterilized at least once a year. Avian tuberculosis is also transmitted through bird droppings and is another common cause of death amongst wild birds, particularly the larger ones. Many of these diseases are better known in domestic poultry; this is certainly true of Fowl Plague and Newcastle Disease which are often collectively known as Fowl Pest. The virus for Newcastle Disease has been isolated in a number of wild bird species which seem to be able to harbour it without ill-effect.

The density independent causes of death are legion. Whilst they are not always important in terms of affecting population, nevertheless the birdwatcher-naturalist could usefully record these deaths in the same way that he records the individual items of food eaten by a bird. Such records, if made consistently, could in time produce useful quantitative data.

Monitoring of the road deaths of birds several years ago showed that deaths of birds occurred most frequently when adults were feeding young in the nest, and at places where road verges were narrow or non-existent and the hedges came close to the tarmac – in fact deaths occurred most frequently in those parts of the road which were also dangerous in human terms.

The effects of oil which has been accidentally spilled or has been illegally discharged at sea and which can kill many thousands of birds and other animals is a continuing menace. Real catastrophes occur when one or more of the supertankers have an accident in an area inhabited by large numbers of seabirds and it is sad to think that such accidents continue to happen. The *Amoco Cadiz* disaster is proof enough.

The effect of polychlorinated biphenyls (PCB's), which was noticed recently by the Beached Bird Survey (see page 70), and the other closely related chlorinated hydrocarbon pesticides, such as Dieldrin, Aldrin, Heptachlor and DDT, has been to kill considerable numbers of birds throughout the world. So much so that ornithologists became seriously concerned over the decline in the populations of many species of birds of prey.

This sort of pollution by man-made chemicals, although in some respects gradually being brought under control, is inevitably going to recur as new products are released with inadequate testing and accidents happen. Wildlife once more will remind mankind what it is doing to the planet.

Natural events such as the various manifestations of the weather can cause the deaths of birds. A very wet spring can drown nests and eggs in holes, and can make the search for food and the feeding of the young such a daunting task that the parents give up. At the other extreme drought may also affect the breeding success of birds and their survival, even though comparatively few species need liquid water to drink and obtain the moisture necessary to them through their food. Another factor is that the ground may become too hard for thrushes to catch worms. P. & E. Willson, who carry out a Garden Bird Feeding Survey suggested in *BTO News No. 84* that a marked decline in the number of birds coming to their feeding station in the autumn of 1976 could have been due to that summer's drought. However, it could just be that the birds did not need to come to the feeding station as the weather was so mild. While on migration strong winds can divert birds to places a great distance from their normal wintering areas. Over a long stretch of the sea contrary winds can exhaust them: I have seen Starlings dropping exhausted into the North Sea only a few hundred metres from the Norfolk coast after battling from the continent against strong westerly winds.

Birds fly into wires, buildings and window panes. They usually fly into windows when they can see light at the other end of a room, presumably as they are under the impression that they are flying through and under cover.

Some causes of death are bizarre. I once rescued a Storm Petrel, which is a bird which only comes to land at night during the breeding season, which had flown onto the upper burrs of a Great Burdock and if I had not released it, would ultimately have died or been killed by some other animal as it hung there.

I have suggested you should record wherever possible the causes of deaths. Try to find out if some use can be made of the bodies of birds. Most museums like good skins so that they have no need to kill others for educational purposes. Scientists wanting bodies of birds, which have died or been accidentally killed, for chemical analysis, publish their requests in *Bird Study*, *Birds* or *British Birds*.

But, if you can find no one who has any scientific need for these bodies, see what you can learn from them yourself before you dispose of them. Look at and sketch them in your notebook; draw them carefully, having measured with a pair of dividers the shape and width of the various parts of the bird. How curved in the beak? Look at the lie of the feathers. How fresh are they? Was the bird moulting? You could also look for feather parasites, but if the body is cool most of them will already have deserted.

Then, with a sharp knife – a scalpel and surgical scissors are better still – you can open the bird up, identify the various internal organs, bones and muscles. If you do this often enough and learn what the inside of a bird looks like under normal conditions you may get some idea of the cause of death. There are great opportunities to learn from accidents.

While the European Kingfisher nests in burrows near streams, other species are terrestrial, feeding on insects, and it is probable that our Kingfisher's large bill was originally evolved as an adaptation to insect-catching and not for fishing.

Above Knot and one Sanderling foraging in wet sands. Length and size of bill and length of legs help to prevent direct competition between them and other shorebirds foraging in the same area (see page 155).

Right Greenfinches in a Cambridgeshire wood tended to eat the hips of the Field Rose *Rosa arvensis* but left the hips of the Dog Rose *Rosa canina*. Have you noted any other food preferences?

Above Modern farming tends towards hedgeless prairies; the gardens of villages have the aspect of a woodland edge or the early stages of the development of a wood and provide a refuge for many species of wildlife.

Below When the Suffolk marshes were flooded during the last war, many, like Minsmere, proved attractive to birds. In 1948 the RSPB leased Minsmere and thoughtful management has provided still more habitats. The RSPB purchased Minsmere in 1977 from part of their £1 million appeal.

What birds eat

Discovering what birds eat really tests your desire to be a birdwatcher-naturalist. The subject, though fascinating, can be extremely complicated and requires enormous patience. However, this should not put you off. There are some comparatively simple things to do. Identifying what plants or animals a bird may be eating may not be too difficult, but the researcher will also want to have an accurate idea about the quantity of each item. As quite often conservation bodies need a scientific evaluation of, for instance, the quantity of food available to birds in the various estuaries around the coast of Britain. They need to know, if barrages are built on the Wash, or if part of Seal Sands are reclaimed, whether there are other estuaries on the east coast of Britain which will be able to supply sufficient food for the displaced birds.

In the 1950s, Dr David Lack and his team at the Edward Grey Institute at Oxford studied the food of tits in nearby Wytham Woods. These studies and the estuarine studies of John Goss-Custard have thrown a new light on the feeding ecology of birds, and whilst the amateur cannot often hope to emulate this work, the published results do show the birdwatcher-naturalist many items which he can look for and record. In spite of the excellence of the work of the professionals there is still much that you can discover for yourself.

Whilst every living creature needs food to keep it alive, a small bird which burns up energy at a furious rate, needs to take about a third of its body weight in food every day to make up for the heat and energy loss. The exact amount depends on the type of food eaten. Large birds need less food because their heat loss is less; being larger creatures they have less surface area in relation to their volume than small birds. At certain times of the year and for certain activities they need to take in extra food. Some need to accumulate extra fat before they migrate and fly long distances; while some males feed their mates before they lay their eggs. Young Manx Shearwaters and similar species put on an enormous amount of fat before they are deserted by their parents and have to learn to fend for themselves.

Birds have managed to exploit almost every habitat and every niche as a hunting ground; they have not been able to dig more than a little way into the ground in search of food, but at sea Long-tailed Ducks regularly dive to 20 metres and can reach 60 metres, but information of the depth at which other diving birds feed is rather limited. Perhaps here is an opportunity for scuba-diving birdwatchers to collect knowledge. Birds hunt in the sky as high as there are insects and other creatures in a sufficient quantity to make it worth their while. To be able to exploit all these niches birds have developed within a general form a huge variety of beak shapes, legs and wing structures. Adaptation to different food sources has probably affected their structure more than any other factor, even the urgent need to escape from predators.

The type of food a bird will eat is influenced by a number of factors, of which the most important is the instinctive hunting methods of the genus. For instance, nearly all flycatchers eat flies and other insects. Most finches eat both animal and vegetable food while crows and gulls are generally omnivorous. The second component in the feeding habits are the characteristic specific habits that give a species a measure of ecological isolation. Here, for instance, the Spotted Flycatcher eats insects, chiefly flies, but rarely worms and berries. Although the food of the Pied Flycatchers is also chiefly insects, including flies, it seems to have a wider range of insect food, in particular the Small Pearl-bordered Fritillary *Clossiana selena*. Some species become highly specific in their eating habits, the slender-billed form of the Nutcracker, although a member of the usually omnivorous crow family, specializes in the seeds of the Arolla Pine *Pinus cembra* and the Bhutan Pine *Pinus excelsa* in the more easterly parts of its range.

The structure of the body, particularly its effect on the way the bird moves, may restrict it to a certain type of habitat; the structure of the beak and talons may localize the hunt and finally local experience of the availability and whereabouts of food items will contribute to the success of the hunt. This local knowledge of the food supply is of great importance and is often not taken into account when people who have been caring for sick or injured birds release them into the wild after several weeks or several months of treatment. This particularly applies to recently cleaned seabirds. We tend to think that the shoals of fish on which the auks feed are everywhere. But they move with the seasons. Auks come into the waters near the breeding cliffs when the sand eels and other small fish are near the surface and most abundant, and from daily contact they get to know in which part of the colony's home waters the fish are to be found. Once a seabird is removed from the sea for any great length of time it will lose touch with the fishing flocks and be considerably handicapped in finding sufficient food when released.

The way in which the beaks, legs or wings have been adapted now most affect the selection of food. Herons and egrets have long legs that enable them to wade deeply into lakes, ponds and even the sea to hunt. Wading birds with their long legs, such as the Bar-tailed Godwit, can also wade deeply in water and still probe beneath the surface and into the mud or sand with their long sensitive bills. Another wader, the Avocet sweeps the surface of the mud below water from side to side with its awl-shaped bill.

At the other extreme Goldfinches, Redpolls and their relatives have rather short legs. They tend to perch on rather thin and flexible twigs which

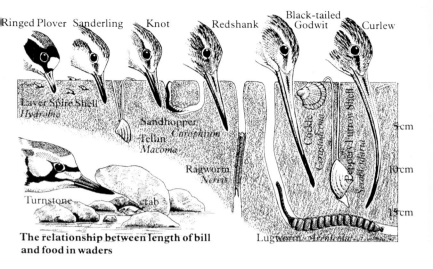

The relationship between length of bill and food in waders

Waders have different bill sizes and lengths of leg, which enable them to forage in different places on the shore line.

bend over so that the bird has to hang on to the twig with its short toes, often nearly upside down. Their short legs help to keep the centre of gravity rather low so that there is less strain on the legs. Short-legged birds also use their feet more commonly in holding food than longer-legged birds. Incidentally, the Goldfinch has a rather thin and pointed bill which enables it to probe quite well for the seeds of a number of the compositae family – dandelions and thistles.

Long pointed wings, or high aspect ratio wings as they are called, are the mark of fast 'pursuit' birds, while the broad-winged birds are either those which soar in the rising thermals or which live in woodland areas and need the ability to manoeuvre through branches. Included in the first group are long-winged insect-eaters such as Swifts, Swallows and Nightjars which need some speed to pursue their prey which they catch with their mouths in mid-air. Included in this group are also the falcons which use their talons to catch birds and insects, and occasionally rodents.

The evenly balanced arrangement of claws are important in wood-peckers, as it enables them to get a better grip on the bark of trees on which most of them hunt. Their strong bills are also useful when digging holes beneath the bark for insects or their larvae, or hammering at acorns which they wedge in cracks in branches or trunks. Green Woodpeckers have largely deserted the trees and prefer ant nests on the ground into which they insert their long tongue and, with its sticky tip, extract the ants or their pupae.

155

Waterfowl, particularly those which swim and dive for their food, have developed webs between their toes: some species may only be partially webbed like the Red-necked Phalarope which is essentially a wader which feeds in the water. At the other extreme, the Shag which hardly ever walks any distance on land has webs between all four toes to drive it through the water when it is hunting for fish amongst the sea wrack. Razorbills and Guillemots propel themselves through the water in their search for fish by beating their wings almost as though they were flying. While the Dipper, an underwater thrush, which hunts for its food amongst the stones in swift-flowing streams, holds out its wings in such a way that the flow of water forces it to the bottom.

The range of different feeding methods and the different food taken is extremely varied and a study of them supports the view that closely related species living in the same habitat do not compete for food. Following this point through there is enormous scope for working even in your own garden or some other habitat well-known to you which is utilized by birds for hunting. What, for instance, are the commonest ways of finding food used by the different species? What sort of hunting perches do the Spotted Flycatchers use? What height are the hunting perches? Do they hunt in the trees or just use part of the tree as a look-out? Do the hunting perches change through the breeding season and does a change indicate a different type of prey? When answering the same sort of questions for other species you may have to list the plants birds use and attempt to determine their use as food or hunting perches throughout the season. Does it change? Do birds hunt in the same place or with the same regularity throughout the day?

It is sometimes impossible to do all this in a professional way in which you can completely document the food species of birds but gradually you should be able to build up a picture of the distribution of birds throughout the habitat.

Casual observations can be useful too. In a wood in which I have been working, up to ten Greenfinches may concentrate in October and November upon the hips of the Field Rose *Rosa arvensis*. By counting the fruit along a ride at regular intervals I was able to see at what speed the hips were eaten. It would have been possible, if I had spared more time from other studies, to have much clearer information upon the proportion of hips eaten by the Greenfinch, Bullfinch and Marsh Tit. The hips of the Dog Rose *Rosa canina* were not touched by these three species. So on your walks in autumn it is worthwhile examining seed production on all sorts of plants as soon as they begin to ripen and then watch to see if they disappear, and try to discover what is eating them. I also watched three Greenfinches feeding for a time on the seeds of Queen Anne's Lace *Anthriscus sylvestris* but again had no time to discover how many days they continued to do this. On my holidays, too, I have been watching Greenfinches and Linnets feeding on the seeds of the Sea Radish *Raphanus maritimus*, Hedge Mustard *Sisymbrium officinale* and Fat Hen *Chenopodium album*.

Bird gardening

I imagine that most birdwatchers with gardens try for one reason or another to attract birds to them. If they are ringers it may be that their only interest is to encourage the birds to enter their traps or mist nets. On the other hand many of us regret that birds are so wild and would like them to be somewhat more confiding – although not so tame that they fall victim to marauding cats or to a neighbour who may resent the damage that some birds can do to plants and vegetables which they fail to protect.

You have to decide what you want your garden for: for recreation – that is somewhere where you and your family can play; for flowers, or vegetables coupled with a secondary interest in birds; or are you primarily interested in birds and willing to set about making a bird garden out of native plants and shrubs as well as some of the more exotic plants which birds willingly use and which have to be obtained from a nurseryman? I fall into the second of these groups: I have become a very keen vegetable gardener and my wife and I like to keep ourselves supplied with vegetables and certain fruits, but obviously I want to see lots of birds around.

The trouble is that when we think or talk about gardens we tend to think very conventionally. I expect that many of the readers of this book will live in fairly modern houses with new gardens comprising flower beds, a small vegetable plot, with a lawn and perhaps a pond or bird bath. Probably, this patch will be duplicated many times in the neighbourhood. If you overlook the whole area from some hill, or imagine yourself looking down from above, ask yourself what type of natural habitat this village or patchwork of houses and gardens most resembles. I am always struck by its resemblance to one or more stages of a woodland edge with rock outcrops (the houses) or a stage in the growth of a woodland. Many gardens have trees of varying ages and heights – the older the better. Some gardens may have shrubs up to 6 metres high. Some will have a field layer up to 1·5 metres and some may have a heavily mown (or grazed) lawn. This is the same sort of structure that you find in woodland, particularly at the edge of natural woodlands which may be spreading into a grassland habitat.

I believe that if you are really trying to provide a garden for birds you must aim towards this basic concept of a woodland edge. You may not have enough room for big trees and may have to concentrate on the lower levels. Perhaps your neighbours are providing trees in their gardens. However, if you do have a tree and it grows too big you can always cut it down and use some of the wood for firewood and leave the rest to provide homes for insects. Then plant another tree. Creating a bird garden takes a long time and if you have come into a fairly new garden and have to plant it yourself you are going to have to wait for several years for it to achieve maturity. However, you have to start somewhere and the garden you lay down may set the pattern for your successors.

When choosing trees for your garden try to plant native ones. It is on native trees, with their associated invertebrate fauna, that most of our birds are accustomed to feed. An Oak takes a very long time to grow but even in its earliest years it is a very beautiful tree and is also a host to a very large number of insects. What native trees you can grow depend upon the soil and climate of your region. The Nature Conservancy Council have produced a useful booklet, *Tree Planting and Wildlife Conservation*. Walnut trees, too, provide delicious nuts providing that you can beat the squirrels and Rooks to them. As in forestry they can be planted fairly close together to start with and thinned out after a few years so that they grow good lateral branches which make foraging much easier for the less agile of the woodland birds. Trees will provide not only an extensive feeding ground but many species will also find in them the height they need to display their dominance.

The first trees to be considered are the fruit trees which in time develop lateral branches with plenty of cracks in which insects can hide. What I am saying is heresy to the keen fruit gardener who all too often tends to shoot birds in fruit trees. But at least two scientists have recently shown that tits, and Blue Tits in particular, eat large numbers of Codling Moth *Cydia pomonella* caterpillars and as apples are damaged more by Codling Moths than by birds I have erected nest boxes for them on my apple trees. Pears as well as other fruit trees can also use the help that birds will give them by eating insects. However, they will not control insects – no predator controls the number of its prey – it may, however, help to dampen the numbers down a little.

Hawthorn *Cragaegus monogyna* is a most valuable shrub to have in the garden. It can be allowed to grow to its full height as a shrub providing a mass of beautiful colour in spring and luscious berries for the Blackbird and Song Thrush, as well as the Redwing and Fieldfare during the autumn. It can also be layered into a hedge where, if it is trimmed once or twice a year (not too early in the year), it will provide thick cover for quite a range of birds such as Blackbirds, Robins, Dunnocks, Wrens, Linnets, Green-finches, Chaffinches and Whitethroats. If it is allowed to grow more than 2 metres high it can also attract the Lesser Whitethroat – in the south-east part of the country, at least. It is also important to allow it a good thick bottom growth.

Another useful natural shrub is the Elder *Alnus glutinosa* with its beautiful cymes of white flowers which, if you do not pick them to make Elder-flower wine or Elder-flower pancakes, will turn into sweet tasting berries which are much favoured by both birds and winemakers. Also when large, the Elder branches and twigs become a hunting ground for warblers and are also suitable as nesting sites for such as the Goldfinch.

Ivy *Hedera helix* tends to have a gloomy reputation, perhaps because it is rather dark and is often found on ruins. Nevertheless it does provide a nesting site for many species and the Song Thrush and Blackbird eat its berries quite voraciously in late March and April, perhaps because there is little else to eat at that time of the year. Sometimes it is alleged that if ivy grows too densely it will strangle the tree, and just as frequently the point is disputed. However, if it is allowed to completely cover the bole of the tree it will eliminate a feeding ground for woodpeckers, Treecreepers and Nuthatches.

Brambles *Rubus fruticosus* in some senses are an awful pest but they do produce nest sites and Blackbirds and other thrushes do eat their berries. It always seems surprizing to me that more are not eaten by these birds. Rowan *Sorbus aucuparia* is another shrub, more properly found in the mountainous districts of the north or higher ground, which bears colourful berries eaten by birds. The Sea Buckthorn *Hippophae rhamnoides* is found on the sandy shores of the east coast and masses of migrants feed on it as soon as they make a landfall on their autumn migration. One native tree under-rated for its berry is the Whitebeam *Sorbus aria*. It is an attractive tree with white flowers and red berries which seem to be voraciously eaten by birds.

A range of berry-bearing shrubs, which generally do not grow more than 2 metres high, including the genera *Berberis* and *Cotoneaster* are important. *Berberis vulgaris* and *Darwinii* both produce berries which are taken by birds but not all the species are equally paleatable. The same applies to *Cotoneaster*. Although Guelder Rose *Vibernum opulus* is said to be good for birds, where I have been watching bushes very few of the berries have been taken by early spring. However, the berries of the Wayfaring Tree *Viburnum lantana* are eaten by thrushes. Our knowledge about which birds take which species of berries is still surprisingly open and someone who would really like to watch these bushes throughout the year could add greatly to the subject. However, you must pay attention to what happens to berries at the end of the winter too, when birds may be so hungry that they eat the less palateable ones. Gamekeepers have much to say in favour of the Snowberry *Symphoricarpus rivularis* but the berries seem to stay on the tree all the winter which, to my mind, is not a good advertisement for the palateability of a berry.

The third structural level is the field layer with plants up to 2 metres or so. I personally am not so likely to wish to plant native species in my garden, although I allow some to flower and produce seed. Queen Anne's Lace or Cow Parsley *Anthriscus sylvestris* is one of the most beautiful and stately plants of the English countryside and I was glad to see Greenfinches which nest in my thick hawthorn hedge eating its seed. I keep a rough area alongside part of my hawthorn hedge and this I only cut once a year. Cow Parsley grows here and in various other rough spots.

Another plant which real gardeners absolutely hate is Fat Hen *Chenopodium album*, but finches are immensely attracted by its seeds and, if

Simple pond with dripping water

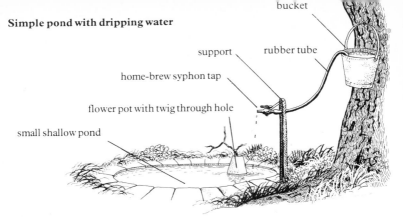

bucket

support   rubber tube

home-brew syphon tap

flower pot with twig through hole

small shallow pond

A system for providing dripping water which will attract birds especially in dry weather can be made simply from 'home brew' equipment.

you can bear to have it around, it will bring in Greenfinches, Linnets and Goldfinches in late summer and early autumn. Bullfinches like Black Bryony *Tamus communus* which, although it is a most attractive creeper, is generally disliked by gardeners. Native Teazel *Dipsacus pullonum* attracts Goldfinches which will also eat some of the more exotic varieties. Many species of the Compositae family are sought after by finches, particularly the Sunflower *Helianthus annuus*, aster *Aster* spp. and many species of thistle, although not many gardeners will tolerate Creeping Thistle *Cirsium arvense*. One of the best sources of information about seeds of wild herbs and shrubs eaten by finches is to be found in Ian Newton's book, *Finches*. It is also a most instructive book on all aspects of finch biology and behaviour.

The bottom or 'open' layer of the garden will usually be lawn or soil. Both are good for birds hunting for insects and other arthropods, as well as for seeds.

Ponds provide water for drinking and bathing. Most birds obtain sufficient moisture from their food but some such as Woodpigeons and Turtle Doves come down regularly to drink, and many others will drink water if it is available. Many people try to attract birds by letting water drip into a container. To do this all you need is a bucket or a container which can hold a fair amount of water. You can set up a syphon and control the rate of dripping with a length of plastic tubing and a small tap, which can be obtained from any home-brewing shop. It is best to let the water drip into a shallow receptacle such as the edge of your pond or even an upturned dustbin lid, sunk into the ground. This, according to Philip Hollom and the late Guy Brownlow, is very attractive to warblers and finches.

In my pond I have put stones which just appear above the surface which allow birds to bathe. Tony Soper recommends a flower pot upside down in the water with a stick or twig through the hole on which Wrens and other small birds such as warblers can perch and slither down to drink.

It is surprising what species will come to your pond particularly when it has matured and the water plants are growing well, encouraging insects of various kinds. On my small pool I found a Green Sandpiper one morning in the last half of June. If you have fish or tadpoles in your pond you may expect visits from Kingfishers and Herons. Both have visited my pond. I have never detected the Kingfisher as causing any serious damage. If he caught anything which my family or I were particularly interested in we certainly did not detect it. The Heron can, however, clean out a Goldfish pond in not time at all. As he is really adapted for eating eels and we like our Goldfish, we try to prevent him from eating them. You can cover the pond with wire netting, but this is unsightly. It is said that a strand of nylon line – fishing line will do – set 60 centimetres back from the edge of the pond and stretched tightly, 15 centimetres above the ground, will stop the Heron. This is because Herons tend to alight away from the water and after looking around move towards it. If their feet hit something fairly invisible and firm they take fright and move off. Never leave loose nylon line lying about as this can 'tie up' birds' legs and cause serious damage. Herons are protected by law so don't shoot them. Another will come along in due course, therefore it is much wiser, in the long run, to protect the pond.

I have been writing about using nature to make your garden attractive to birds, and also making nature provide the food and shelter. You can also attract birds by setting up bird tables and nest boxes. Bird tables can be made easily or can be purchased from the RSPB. They are essentially a board with an edge to prevent the food being knocked off. Some have shelters over them which prevent the food becoming wet. They should be set at least one metre above ground to make it more difficult for cats and squirrels to get at them. The wooden support can be sheathed in a length of slippery plastic drain pipe. The problem of Starlings and House Sparrows taking too much food is difficult to overcome. I have no satisfactory solution although some people have made wooden tops to their bird tables with holes big enough for Blue Tits to get through but then only Blue Tits can feed, and hanging food baskets really cater for them. I have tried putting food out in different places which disperses the different species for a time. It is essential to clean and sterilize bird tables from time to time to avoid the risk of *Salmonella* infection. You should not leave out so much food that it is left lying about.

A variety of different makes of seeds are available from pet shops and are advertised in the different bird magazines, and I imagine that most people will, if they are going to buy seed, buy it in bulk from a supplier. I used to make up my own mixture at one time, with Black Rape, Millet, Hemp, Niger, Sunflower and Peanut. Dunnocks used to love Blue Maw, a poppy seed, which they take from the ground.

On the bird table you can put not only seeds, but household scraps and fruit, whether berries or the rotten part of apples. Do leave rotten apples under the trees – thrushes particularly the winter visitors, love them.

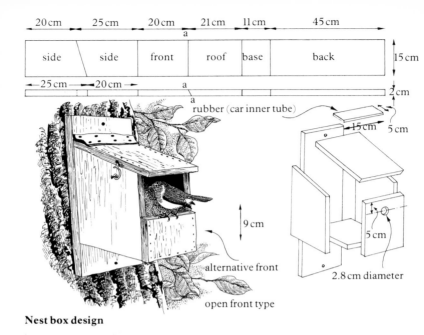

Nest box design

Nest boxes can be made from a variety of simple plans which are specifically designed for a range of birds.

Some people hang out nuts – for some reason those in red bags prove very attractive to Siskins – and others jam nuts or fat into the bark of trees in their garden. This is fine for tits and others that can hang on to the sides of the tree, but Blackbirds and other thrushes need flat surfaces.

Putting up nest boxes is a good idea particularly in new gardens which have not developed a wide range of nest sites. Most people buy the standard tit nest box, not realizing the other possibilities. Different species of bird need different designs of nest box. One simple type of nest 'box' can be made from half a coconut, with a hole in the base for drainage. If it is placed in a wall climbing shrub like a wisteria it will make an ideal nest site for Spotted Flycatchers, which often make use of old Blackbirds' nests. They also use small open-fronted nest boxes with base dimensions of 15 × 9 centimetres. Swifts, as the late Dr Lack demonstrated, used nest boxes if they are provided. These are 46 × 20 centimetres wide by 14 centimetres deep with an entrance hole in the base and an inspection lid at the opposite end. It is fitted under the eaves of the house at least 3 metres above the ground. Artificial House Martin nests are more difficult to make unless you have a kiln in which you can bake clay. However, they are occasionally advertised for sale. The Tawny Owl is another species whose breeding distribution you can help by making a nest box. This should be made from wooden planks at least 75 centimetres long and 20 centimetres wide with a square base which must have at least half a dozen drainage holes. The box should be lined with peat or sawdust before it is hung in position under a bough at about 30° from the vertical. The details of these and other nest box designs can be found in the BTO Field Guide No. 3 *Nestboxes*.

Comparatively few people would appear to have attempted to artificially thicken vegetation around trees, or thicken forks in branches in hedges by inserting handfulls of dried leaves for Wrens. This is something that used to be practised on the continent. By tying a spruce branch to a trunk with strings about 30 centimetres apart it is possible to provide a space in which thrushes might nest. There are many other ways in which these simple aids to nest building can be applied.

Perhaps, at this point I ought to say something about two problems that arise in bird gardens. The first one is the problem of pesticides. There has been a lot of concern over the last twenty years about the effects of certain organo-chlorine chemicals. Many of them are now banned, at least for garden use. However, all pesticides should be used with discretion and it is best to use them only when you really need to against a pest which you are sure is harming your plants. It is a waste of money using insecticides on something which is doing no damage. Do not use a pesticide unless you know what it is; the active ingredients should be stated on the container label. There are some pesticides which the RSPB feels are relatively speaking non-poisonous to birds and mammals and are not persistant. These are Derris or Rotenone, Pyrethium, Malathion and Carbanyl. The RSPB produce a booklet called *Pesticides and the Gardener*.

The second problem concerns the activities of cats. One extreme view says that cats should be got rid of at any cost. The other extreme says that cats only kill birds if they are not fed properly, which in my experience is nonesense; good feeding will probably make the cat a more effective hunter. There is no proof one way or the other as to what effect cats have on local bird populations. Luckily my family's cat – not mine – is very territorially minded and generally keeps other cats away. However, when I have to take action to save a nest I rely on 'shushing'; occasionally a lump of dried earth lobbed to fall just short of the cat so that the lump breaks open and harmlessly spatters the offender with dust will do the trick – if the throwing motion has not been enough to frighten it away. Cats, like birds, can be a nuisance in the wrong place. But there is no justification for using cruel methods to get rid of them.

There are a number of very good books which take bird gardening much further, for example, the *RSPB Book of Garden Birds* by Linda Bennett published by Hamlyn, Tony Soper's *The New Bird Table Book* published by Pan, and Maxwell Knight's *Bird Gardening*, published by Ian Henry Publications.

Conservation and bird protection

Man is one of the most important agents in affecting the distribution of birds or even affecting their chances of survival in the world today. In the comparatively short time that man has been of sufficient a force he has altered the face of the Earth. Once Britain was covered in forests whereas now there are towns, pastures and 'prairies', and areas once rich in lakes and marshes have been drained. In his need for food, for other raw materials of life, for more land, for more airports, for more fresh water, man continues to alter the natural environment. He is continually finding new methods of removing natural objects which were an impediment to his clearances. He corralls large numbers of holidaymakers in sensitive areas like the tops of the Cairngorm mountains, or builds marinas and oil platforms, rendering estuaries sterile where only twenty years ago the Redshank and the Curlew and many other waders could feed undisturbed. These estuaries are often vital to wintering waders from Russia and, in hard winters, also waders from Northern Europe. All of which is tragic for the birds as the numbers of these estuaries are limited; when they have gone, there is nowhere else for these birds to go.

The RSPB, which is particularly active in giving evidence at public enquiries where a site of ornithological importance is threatened, reports that in recent years Secretaries of State have overruled their Inspectors on at least four occasions. At Nigg Bay in the Cromarty Firth, at Cliffe on the north Kent marshes, at Seal Sands in the estuary of the River Tees and at Arne, in Dorset. Here, Inspectors or especially appointed panels decided that the arguments for reclamation of the sites to build refineries or factories or, as in the case at Arne, for ball-clay winning were weak and that there were positive reasons on nature conservation grounds against reclamation of any but a small sector of the sites. However, successive Secretaries of State have overturned these recommendations.

It is not only on the larger scale that the natural habitat of the wild birds is being lost, but on a local scale those of us who live in the country see the continual erosion of the cover in which birds live. At least in East Anglia and East Midlands more hedges and trees are going every year. This is in spite of the work of the Farming and Wildlife Advisory Group (FWAG) which has persuaded many of the bigger farmers to replant in areas where trees and hedges have been torn down. The small farmer and sometimes the young farmer can be somewhat thoughtless in their activities, and remove hedges without really thinking if their action is useful or necessary.

Furthermore, modern hedge-cutting machines allow very few young trees to grow through the hedge and consequently the vast majority of trees in hedges are old. What happens when they die? I think we shall be seeing more and more treeless areas in the arable counties. Very often this is a result simply of too much tidiness.

We can act as conservationists on our own small patches, indeed, we all should try to do this as conservation is really a philosophy for living. It is sad that not one of the books that have been written on the subject of conservation in Britain stands out as a standard or classic work and we have to go to the United States to find the technical and descriptive books which give the clearest ideas and feelings as to what is conservation.

I prefer Raymond Dassman's definition of conservation given in his book, *Environmental Conservation*, to any other. It is, 'the rational use of the environment to provide a high quality of living for mankind'. The essential word in this definition is 'use', which is in turn qualified by the word 'rational'. I think that many naturalists have never really accepted that conservation means use; use by farmers, by hunters, by foresters, even industrialists. Many of them use the word conservation when they really mean nature protection or wildlife management. Both bird and nature protection and wildlife management are part of conservation, as much as is farming, harvesting a crop of wildfowl or pheasants or any other proper use of the natural environment.

The word conservation is badly misused. You read of conserving ancient houses or conservation areas in towns. Until European Conservation Year 1970 the word protection was used and it still is the best word for many of these activities. There is nothing old-fashioned about good honest protection where it is needed. I have been basically a protector of birds from the unwise uses of the environment by man and I have also been a wildlife manager in the sense that I have in my early days with the RSPB manipulated land to provide good habitats for birds, and indeed I still do in my own back garden. I hope too that, in my own outlook on life, I am a conservationist in the sense that I think it may be sensible for farmers to rationalize their field sizes, and use certain chemicals against pests; that it is perfectly legitimate to shoot and eat certain birds; that some building for industry and housing is necessary. But it is also my duty to ensure that the evidence I have relating to the scientific value of the land to be used for any of these purposes, is accurate and is properly presented to any court of enquiry held to assess the differing point of views as to what is 'rational use'.

A famous wildlife manager and conservationist who also wrote beautifully about conservation was Aldo Leopold and some of his philosophy shines out in his book *Sand County Almanack*, a collection of essays originally published in 1949 by Oxford University Press, but still in print and still worth reading. His chapters entitled, 'Conservation Ethic' and 'Land Ethic' still have a message for us. Whilst Dassman's book supplies the science of environmental management Aldo Leopold is the philosopher.

Birds share the environment with man and many other creatures. Their song, their movement and their colours make them conspicuous and this conspicuousness makes them in turn good indicators of the way in which man or nature is changing the environment. We have already seen that the drought in the Sahel region of North Africa reduced the numbers of Whitethroats and Sand Martins visiting Britain. There may well be other natural disasters within the geographical ranges of birds visiting Britain which have reduced the numbers of some species but which are in areas too remote for us to hear about.

Birds have also been indicators of the more long-term ways in which man has affected his environment. By changing the vegetation of Britain from largely forest to one which is largely agricultural and built up, man has obviously altered the composition of the communities to the disadvantage of some species but to the advantage of others. The drainage of the Fens was disadvantageous for Bitterns, Bearded Tits, Black Terns and Avocets, but advantageous for Skylarks amongst others. The clearance of forests and introduction of sheep by Neolithic man, and rabbits by the Normans, may have reduced the number of forest birds but was advantageous for Wheatears and other species which prefer to hunt over short-grazed turfs. However, the reduction in the number of rabbits following the spread of myxomatosis in the mid-1950s also meant that in lowland areas, grass grew longer again and Wheatear numbers were considerably reduced, as were those of the Stone-curlews.

The total numbers of birds has probably not declined: the numbers of some species have declined, but others have risen. Indeed it is rather interesting to note that in spite of all the changes in the environment to which man and nature have subjected birds, the number of species breeding in the British Isles has been increasing since 1940.

A number of voluntary organizations are involved in bird protection and conservation. First and foremost is the Royal Society for the Protection of Birds with a membership of over a quarter of a million, which is still growing, and with more than 80 reserves protecting birds totalling about 40,000 hectares. With money supplied by its members it is continually adding more reserves of ornithological interest. On these reserves, on advice from its own Research Department, it manages the land to provide optimum living conditions for the birds that live there. It also provides special protection for rare breeding birds like the Osprey. The Conservation Planning Department collects evidence on the ornithological value of sites which are threatened by agricultural or industrial development and also gives evidence at public enquiries. The Education Section seeks to influence public opinion by educating the young through teachers, through its Young Ornithologists' Club, and its excellent quarterly magazine *Bird Life*. The Investigation Branch tries to track down those who are misusing birds and committing offences against the Protection of Birds Act 1954–67. The RSPB is of such a stature that it now has its own Political and International Branch. Members are encouraged to join Local Members

Groups which aim to help the RSPB to raise more money for reserves, to educate and inform through lectures and field outings. Sometimes, they carry out field investigations, although this is usually the province of the British Trust for Ornithology or the local Bird Clubs. The Society also publishes a colourful quarterly magazine, *Birds*.

The British Trust for Ornithology is for the more scientifically orientated and, by the corporate research of their members, it has investigated the distribution of breeding species throughout the British Isles and the *Atlas of Breeding Birds in Britain and Ireland* by Dr J. T. R. Sharrock is the result of these investigations. The BTO has also been compiling a register of sites of ornithological importance. It co-ordinates bird ringing throughout the country, and from year to year runs a number of special enquiries into the summer or winter distribution or special habits of our birds. The results of these enquiries provide valuable data to ensure the better protection and conservation of our wild birds.

The County Naturalists' Trusts have a field of interest which covers all wildlife. Nearly every country has its own Trust, although the Scottish Naturalists' Trust caters for the whole of Scotland. One of the main functions of Trusts is to ensure the better protection and conservation of wildlife within their counties by acquiring nature reserves, running education programmes, and influencing as far as possible local authorities and, particularly, local planning authorities in order to safeguard areas of special scientific importance. Because Trusts have few paid staff they rely enormously on voluntary help from their members both in their offices and in the field. The work of the Trust is co-ordinated by the Society for the Promotion of Nature Conservation.

These three bodies are all non-governmental organizations, and I must briefly mention here the Nature Conservancy Council, a government department, which was established to advise central and local government on nature conservation matters. It has also the powers to establish National Nature Reserves, of which it now has a very extensive range; it also undertakes some research. Although it does not have subscribers there is close co-operation amongst the NCC and the main conservation bodies.

What can we do to help as birdwatcher-naturalists? By joining your local Conservation Corps, often organized by the local RSPB Member Groups or County Trusts – particularly if you are feeling young and vigorous – or the national body which is the British Trust for Conservation Volunteers, you will be making a direct contribution to the effort. Some people feel that only when they are helping to manage wildlife by cutting down something, planting trees or clearing lakes and rivers, are they being conservationists. But wildlife management is only one part of conservation. The wildlife of the area needs monitoring before this stage of management can be started; someone also needs to monitor the effect of the changes afterwards. So when you say, 'I want to do something for conservation', do understand there is a lot you can do without cutting something down.

No one who is interested in birds for scientific reasons or, who as a bird lover, enjoys seeing birds around can, these days, avoid the responsibility of doing something to ensure their better protection and conservation. The simplest thing you can do is to support the main organization for the protection of birds, which is the RSPB, also join one of its Local Members Groups. If you are a keen birdwatcher-naturalist who would like to take part in some corporate ornithological research, then you should join the BTO as well. At the same time you should join your local bird club and if your interests extend beyond birds you should also support your local Naturalists' Trust. For it is with your own parish, district, county or vice-county area that you have the opportunity of making your personal contribution to bird protection and conservation.

The essential thing is to know your own area well and the numbers of birds that may be found in it. This may sound an incredibly dull sort of occupation to many people who perhaps like to go off to areas where a wide variety of birds can be seen regularly and where there is a good chance of something pretty unusual turning up. But over the years I have found that the long-term study, even in the ornithologically dull area in which I live, can produce interesting results, and even here the occasional rarity turns up in spring and summer. This type of study will show changes in population level and following on from this you will want to know whether the changes you are observing are a reflection of a national trend or are a purely local event. In the mid-1970s Coal Tits and Goldcrests began to breed in my local deciduous wood – an unusual habitat for these species – but reference to other birdwatchers in the county and the Common Birds Census told me that the increase in these two species was part of the national pattern.

In 1960, 1961 and 1962 local amateur birdwatchers recorded large numbers of finches, Woodpigeons and other birds which were dead or dying. As a result a joint committee of the BTO, RSPB and the Game Research Association (now the Game Conservancy) collated these records and published reports which showed the huge scale on which the birds were being killed. The RSPB commissioned, at some expense, complicated chemical analyses which detected substantial quantities of toxic chemicals within the bodies. From 1961 to 1962 the Ministry of Agriculture and the Nature Conservancy (as it was then) took over investigation. Gradually the chemicals were withdrawn, sometimes voluntarily by the agrochemical industry and later by statute.

Unfortunately, while these chemicals might be controlled it would appear to me that modern pesticides are still indirectly affecting the numbers of certain species in our avifauna. Unfortunately we do not know the population figures for such species as Swifts, Swallows and Cuckoos, perhaps from the 1920s and 1930s, to show whether the numbers of Swifts, for example, that flew over our villages then are the same as those that fly over them now. I never kept an account of the number of Cuckoos I could hear from my house when I came here fifteen years ago. But I heard them fairly regularly. Now if I hear one Cuckoo one day in the summer from my house it is exceptional. Yet where pesticides are not commonly used in various parts of the British Isles they sing and can be seen frequently, so the apparent decline of the Cuckoo is unlikely to be connected with the climate, but more with a general reduction of insects due to 'clean' farming, insecticide spraying, herbicide spraying and so on over vast areas of the country. Since there is still the future to cater for, and since other catastrophic things are likely to happen which will affect our wildlife, what we are doing now, or should be doing, is providing an accurate basis to which future birdwatchers can return to see how populations have changed. In an earlier chapter I have mentioned the BTO's Common Birds Census which is an accurate annual survey of one piece of land. I also believe that the regular records made in your own district of the number of birds seen and passed on to your recorder can have future value.

Another important point about knowing your own area and recording what you have seen is that you can determine at once if something is going wrong and either take action yourself if it is within your capability, or draw the attention of the appropriate authority to the problem. If there are proposals for industrial developments or roads, marinas and so on, which threaten some area which has special ornithological importance, you will already have some evidence as to the importance of the site. The evidence of the local birdwatcher has been used in a number of public enquiries of local and national importance in recent years. The information you can gain may have an intrinsic merit and be a study whose results are worth publishing in their own right. It will also mean that you can also act as a very well informed watchdog for a local organization and even a national one such as the RSPB.

Looking into the lives of birds a postscript

I began this book with a short glimpse into the lives of two birds; first, the Chough, a rather uncommon species which inhabits beautiful places, and second, the Bullfinch, which is common enough and, sadly, considered a pest by some who live in the south-east of the country. What I tried to do in those opening paragraphs and what I have been trying to do throughout this book is to show you that there is more to birdwatching than just identification – fun though this may be. I have tried to encourage you to enrich still further your interest in birds by looking into their lives, by watching quietly, by recording, by asking yourself – and others – questions and by trying to interpret what you have seen. In a book of this size I have been able to describe only a fraction of the variety and intricacy of their behaviour, their migrations, their courtship, their nesting and how they live with other creatures. There is so much to read; so much to find out for yourself; so much to talk about with friends and neighbours; so much to enthral and satisfy; so much that invites you to understand not just the birds' natural environment but your own.

Appendices

Appendix I National bird magazines

The following list of periodicals will help you to keep up-to-date with your birdwatching (see page 30). They vary in their approach depending on the outlook of the organization which publishes them and are listed in the order they appear in the text.

Birds Published quarterly by the RSPB and sent free to members. This is the most popular of the bird journals illustrated by coloured photographs and paintings.

Bird Life Published by the Young Ornithologists' Club six times a year. Illustrated with coloured paintings and photographs; includes articles, projects and competitions.

British Birds Published monthly by MacMillan Journals Ltd., 3 Little Essex Street, London, WC2R 3LF. A readable magazine for all British and Irish birdwatchers and, at the same time, an important scientific journal.

Bird Study Published quarterly by the BTO and sent free to members. An important scientific journal publishing papers which are often the work of corporate research by the Trust's members.

BTO News Published by the BTO seven times a year and sent free to members. Contains BTO news and news of other birdwatching activities.

Ibis Published quarterly by British Ornithologists' Union and sent free to members. The most serious of the scientific journals; contains papers on all aspects of ornithology.

Irish Wildbird Conservancy News Published quarterly by IWC. Gives plenty of up-to-date information on the birds of Ireland, as well as general ornithological activities.

Ringing and Migration Published annually by the BTO. Aims to publish conventional ringing studies on such subjects as migration and population dynamics as well as moulting, weights and field taxonomy.

Wildfowl Published annually by the Wildfowl Trust. This journal publishes papers on the biology and behaviour of the waterfowl of the world, and the places in which they live.

Nature in Wales Published twice yearly by the Naturalists' Trusts of West Wales, North Wales and Radnor and is sent free to members. Includes papers on all aspects of natural history in Wales; contains the *Welsh Bird Report*.

Scottish Birds Published quarterly by the Scottish Ornithologists' Club and is sent free to members. Devoted entirely to the birds and ornithology of Scotland; contains the *Scottish Bird Report*.

Appendix IIa The basic library

The five field guides all have something to offer; which you choose depends upon your experience and whether or how far you wish to travel (see page 23).

Bruun, B., and Singer, A. (1970). *The Hamlyn Guide to the Birds of Britain and Europe*. (revised 1978). Hamlyn.

Heinzel, H., Fitter, R. and Parslow, J. (1972). *The Birds of Britain and Europe with North Africa and the Middle East*. Collins.

Peterson, R., Mountford, G., and Hollom, P. A. D. (1954). *A Field Guide to the Birds of Britain and Europe* (third edition 1974). Collins.

Saunders, D. (1975). *RSPB Guide to British Birds*. Hamlyn.

Scott, B., and Forest, D. (1976). *The Bird Watcher's Key*. Warne.

The following five books give you additional basic facts about the ways of life of the birds of Britain and Europe. One or more is an essential feature in a birdwatcher's library.

Cramp, S. and Simmons, K. E. L. (eds.) (1978). *Handbook of the Birds of Europe, the Middle East and North Africa*. Seven volumes, to be published over the next ten years. Oxford University Press.

Hayman, P. and Burton, P. (1976). *The Bird Life of Britain*. Mitchell Beazley in association with the RSPB.

Hollom, P. A. D. (1952). *The Popular Handbook of British Birds*. Fourth edition (revised 1968). Witherby.

Reader's Digest (1969). *The Book of British Birds*. Drive Publications Ltd.

Van Tyne, J. and Berger, A. J. (1976). *Fundamentals of Ornithology*. John Wiley & Sons.

Appendix IIb Key works

A list of key works for identifying various groups of birds or which are more profound studies of various aspects of birds and their biology and behaviour.

Alexander, W. B. (1963). *Birds of the Ocean*. (revised edition). G. P. Putnam & Sons.

Armstrong, E. A. (1958). *The Folklore of Birds*. (revised 1970). Dover Publications.

Armstrong, E. A. (1965). *The Ethology of Bird Display and Behaviour*. Dover Publications.

Armstrong, E. A. (1973). *A Study of Bird Song*. Dover Publications.

Armstrong, E. A. (1975). *Discovering Bird Song*. Shire Publications.

Atkinson-Willes, G. L. (ed.) (1963). *Wildfowl in Great Britain*. H.M.S.O.

British Ornithologists' Union. (1971). *The Status of Birds in Britain and Ireland*. Blackwell Scientific Publications.

Brown, L. (1976). *British Birds of Prey*. (New Naturalist Series). Collins.

Campbell, B. and Ferguson-Lees, J. (1972). *A Guide to Birds' Nests*. Constable.

Cramp, S., Bourne, W. R. P., Saunders, D. (1974). *The Seabirds of Britain and Ireland*. Collins.

Dasman, R. (1959). *Environmental Conservation*. John Wiley & Sons.

Dorst, J. (1962). *The Migrations of Birds*. Heinemann.

Eastwood, E. (1967). *Radar Ornithology*. Methuen & Co.

Elton, C. (1971). *Animal Ecology*. Sidgwick & Jackson.

Ferguson-Lees, J., Hockcliffe, Q. and Zweeres, K. (1975). *A Guide to Bird-watching in Europe*. Bodley Head.

Fisher, J. (1966). *The Shell Bird Book*. Ebury Press and Michael Joseph.

Fisher, J. & Flegg, J. J. M. (1974). *Watching Birds*. T. & A. D. Poyser.

Flegg, J. J. M. (1972). *Binoculars, Telescopes & Cameras*. British Trust for Ornithology. Guide No. 14.

Flegg, J. J. M. & Glue, D. E. (1971). *Nestboxes*. British Trust for Ornithology. Guide No. 3.

Gooders, J. (1967). *Where to Watch Birds*. André Deutsch.

Gooders, J. (1970). *Where to Watch Birds in Europe*. André Deutsch.

Gooders, J. (1975). *How to Watch Birds*. André Deutsch.

Gruson, E. S. (1976). *A Checklist of the Birds of the World*. Collins.

Harrison, C. J. O. (1975). *A Field Guide to the Nests, Eggs and Nestlings of British and European Birds*. Collins.

Jellis, R. (1977). *Bird Sounds and their Meaning*. BBC Publications.

Knight, M. (1977). *Bird Gardening*. Ian Henry Publications.

Lack, D. (1954). *The Natural Regulation of Animal Numbers*. Clarendon Press. (Dr Lack wrote many other books of great scientific value on population and ecological problems.)

Lack, D. (1974). *Evolution Illustrated by Waterfowl*. Blackwell Scientific Publications.

Leopold, A. (1968). *A Sand County Almanack*. Oxford University Press.

Marchington, J. and Clay, A. (1974). *An Introduction to Bird and Wildlife Photography*. Faber & Faber.

Margoschis, R. (1977). *Recording Natural History Sounds*. Print and Press Services.

Murton, R. K. (1971). *Man and Birds*. (New Naturalist Series). Collins.

Nature Conservancy Council (1974). *Tree Planting and Wildlife Conservation*. The Nature Conservancy Council.

Newton, I. (1972). *Finches*. (New Naturalist Series). Collins.

Ogilvie, M. A. (1975). *Ducks of Britain and Europe*. T. & A. D. Poyser.

Ogilvie, M. A. (1978). *Wild Geese*. T. & A. D. Poyser.

Owen, M. (1977). *Wildfowl of Europe*. MacMillan.

Prater, A. J., Marchant, J. H. & Vuorinen, J. (1977). *Guide to the identification and ageing of Holarctic Waders*. British Trust for Ornithology. Guide No. 17.

Parslow, J. (1973). *Breeding Birds of Britain and Ireland*. T. & A. D. Poyser.

Perrins, Christopher (1974). *Birds*. (Countryside Series). Collins.

Porter, R. F., Willis, I., Christensen, S. & Nielson, B. P. (1974). *Flight Identification of European Raptors*. T. & A. D. Poyser.

Sharrock, J. T. R. (1976). *The Atlas of Breeding Birds in Britain and Ireland*. British Trust for Ornithology, Irish Wildbird Conservancy and T. & A. D. Poyser.

Snow, David W. (1976). *The Web of Adaptation*. Collins.

Svensson, L. (1970). *Identification Guide to European Passerines*. (revised 1975). Swedish Museum of Natural History.

Thielcke, G. A. (1976). *Bird Sounds*. Ann Arbor Science Library. The University of Michigan Press.

Thompson, Sir A. Landsborough (1964). *A New Dictionary of Birds*. Nelson.

Thorpe, W. H. (1956). *Learning and Instinct in Animals*. (second revised edition 1963). Methuen.

Thorpe, W. H. (1961). *Bird Song*. Cambridge University Press.

Voous, K. H. (1977). *List of Recent Holarctic Bird Species*. British Ornithologists' Union.

Willis, A. J. (1973). *Introduction to Plant Ecology*. George Allen & Unwin.

Welty, Joel Carl (1964). *The Life of Birds*. Constable.

Williamson, K. (1960–1974). *Identification for Ringers*. (1) *Acrocephalus* and *Hippolais*; (2) *Phylloscopus*; and (3) *Sylvia*. British Trust for Ornithology.

Witherby, H. F., Jourdain, F. C. R., Ticehurst, C. B., Tucker, B. W. (1938). *The Handbook of British Birds*. H. F. & G. Witherby.

Appendix IIc Single species studies

I have included in this part of the appendix only a very short list of books that describe the life histories of single species, but I have tried to include those which are still in print or which have been published recently. There are many more excellent studies which have to be sought for on the second-hand market.

Snow, D. W. (1958). *A Study of Blackbirds*. George Allen & Unwin.
Lack, D. (1956). *Swifts in a Tower*. Chapman & Hall.
Lack, D. (1965). *The Life of the Robin*. Fontana.
Watson, Donald (1977). *The Hen Harrier*. T. & A. D. Poyser.
Murton, R. K. (1965). *The Woodpigeon*. (New Naturalist Series). Collins
Tubbs, C. R. (1974). *The Buzzard*. David & Charles.
Nethersole-Thompson, D. (1966). *The Snow Bunting*. Oliver & Boyd.
Nethersole-Thompson, D. (1973). *The Dotterel*. Collins.
Nethersole-Thompson, D. (1975). *Pine Crossbills*. T. & A. D. Poyser.
Nelson, J. B. (1978). *The Gannet*. T. & A. D. Poyser.

Appendix III Bird clubs

This list includes the organizations whose chief interest is the study or protection of birds. The interest of some is world-wide, others are limited to Britain or even the oceans of the world. Regretfully, it is impossible to list all the county or town bird clubs and RSPB Members Groups. If you wish to find out if there is a club in your district, first ask at your local library; if they do not know of any you can write to one of the national organizations or the Council for Nature, Zoological Gardens, Regent's Park, London NW1 4RY. Send a stamped addressed envelope and remember that answering questions is not really the task of these organizations so send a donation to pay for the staff time you have diverted from its priority duties.

Army Bird Watching Society, Lieutenant-Colonel N. Clayden (retired), MOD Defence Lands, 4 Tolworth Towers, Surbiton, Surrey.

British Ornithologists' Union, c/o The Zoological Society of London, Regent's Park, London NW1 4RY. Publishes *Ibis*.

British Trust for Ornithology, Beech Grove, Tring, Herts. Publishes *Bird Study*, *BTO News*, *Ringing and Migration*.

International Council for Bird Preservation, c/o British Museum (Natural History), Cromwell Road, London SW7.

The Irish Wildbird Conservancy, c/o Royal Irish Academy, 19 Dawson Street, Dublin 2. Publishes *IWC News* and comprehensive *Annual Report* and *Conservation Review*.

Royal Air Force Bird Watching Society, Squadron Leader D. Hollin, O.C., J.S.P.I., Royal Air Force, Wyton, Cambridgeshire.

Royal Naval Birdwatching Society, Hon. Sec. 'Melrose', 23, St. David's Road, Southsea, Hants. Publishes *Sea Swallow*.

Royal Society for the Protection of Birds, The Lodge, Sandy, Beds. SG19 2DL. Publishes *Birds*.

Scottish Ornithologists' Club, 21, Regent Terrace, Edinburgh.

Sea Bird Group, c/o RSPB, The Lodge, Sandy, Beds. SG19 2DL. Publishes *Annual Report*.

The Society for the Promotion of Nature Conservation, The Green, Nettleham, Lincoln LN2 2NR. Publishes *Conservation News*. This is not a bird club but sponsors the County Naturalists' Trusts.

Wildfowl Trust, Slimbridge, Gloucestershire GL2 7BT. Publishes *Wildfowl* and *Wildfowl Trust Magazine*.

Young Ornithologist's Club, The Lodge, Sandy, Beds. SG19 2DL; for young ornithologists up to the age of 18. Publishes *Bird Life* and a newsletter.

Index

Numbers in italics refer to illustrations